Chapter 1

T0417589

nepo
colors

Kiss the Gunner's Daughter

YO HO HO AND A BOTTLE OF *BLOODY* RUM. ISN'T THAT HOW PIRATE STORIES ARE *SUPPOSED* TO START?

WELL THIS *AIN'T* OF THEM STORIES.

IF YER LOOKIN' FOR A PLACE WHERE *X MARKS* THE SPOT, JUS' KEEP A LOOKIN' CUZ I'M TA TELLIN' YA A TALE OF...

VENGEANCE.

FREE PORT TOWNSHIP, GRAND BAHAMA, MAY 1718.

MY NAME'S HANNA,

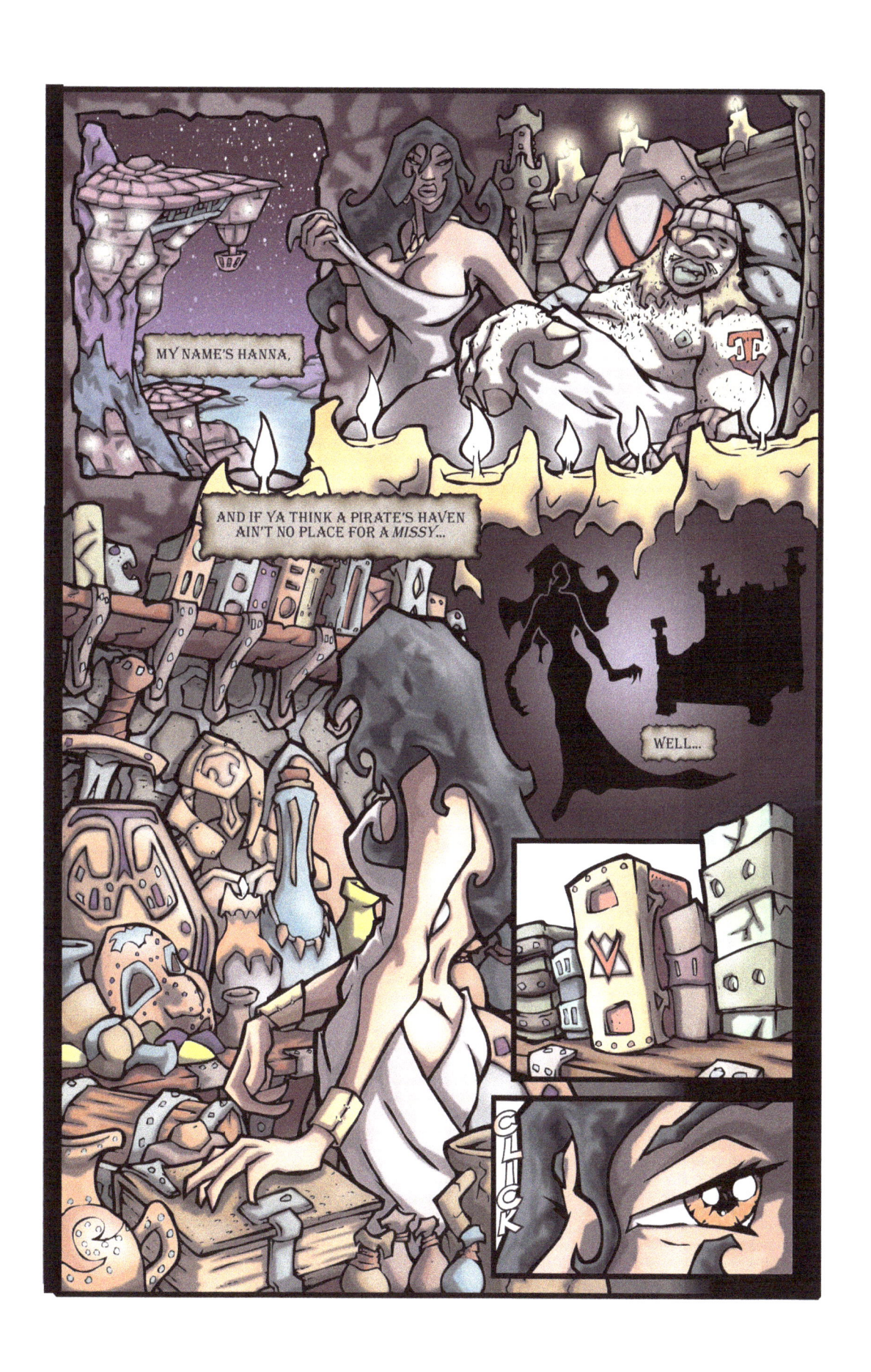

AND IF YA THINK A PIRATE'S HAVEN AIN'T NO PLACE FOR A *MISSY*...

WELL...

CLICK

YOU'RE RIGHT.

DONCHA MOVE A *MUSCLE*.

NOT A *TWITCH*.

'S'NOT VERY SPORTIN'---

YOU *STEALIN'* ME LOG BOOK.

BUT I AIN'T NO *ORDINARY* MISSY.

THIS? A LOG BOOK?

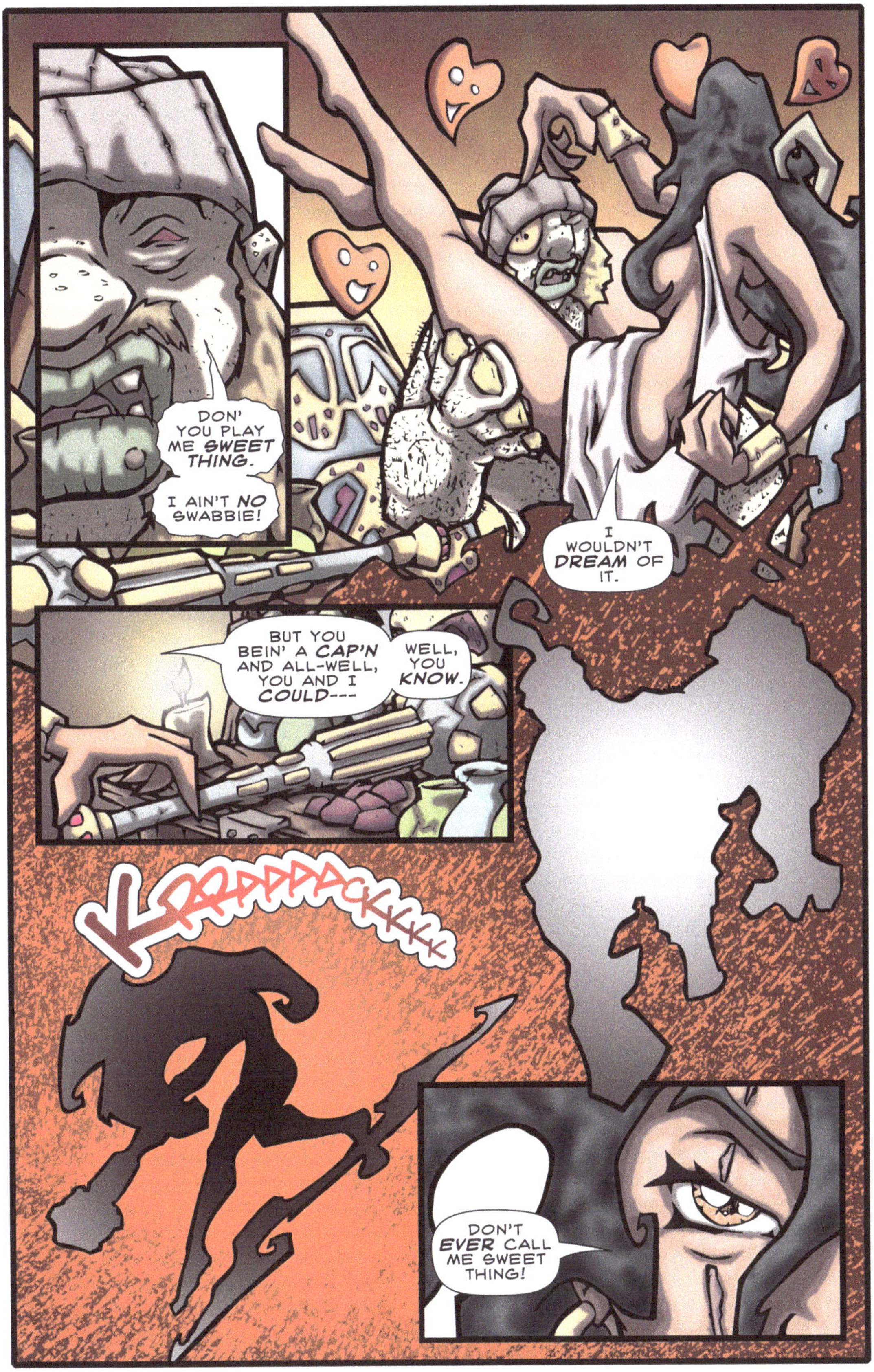
DON' YOU PLAY ME SWEET THING.
I AIN'T NO SWABBIE!
I WOULDN'T DREAM OF IT.
BUT YOU BEIN' A CAP'N AND ALL-WELL, YOU AND I COULD---
WELL, YOU KNOW.
KRRRPPPACKKKKK
DON'T EVER CALL ME SWEET THING!

LIKE I SAYS, I AIN'T NO *ORDINARY* MISSY.

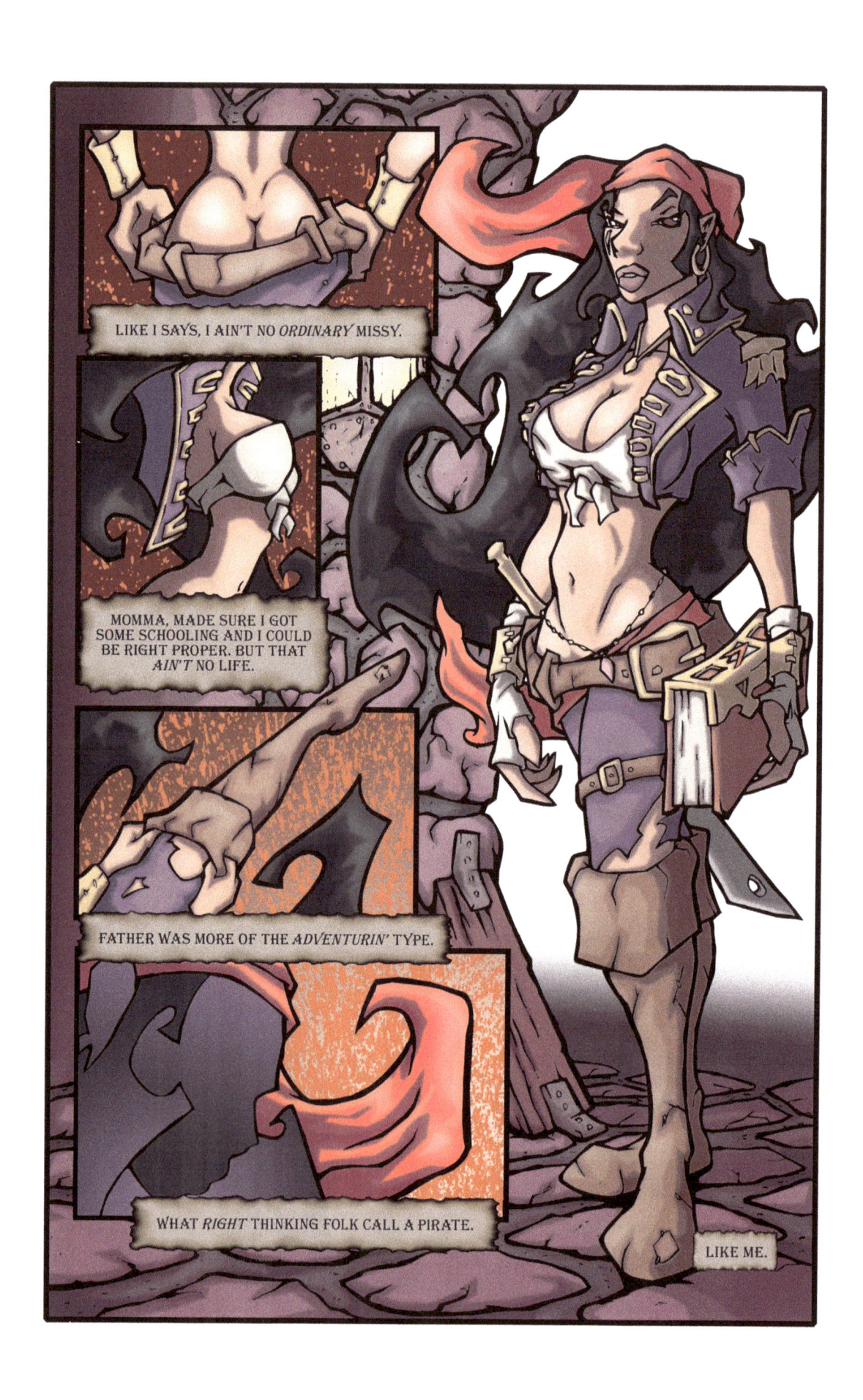

MOMMA, MADE SURE I GOT SOME SCHOOLING AND I COULD BE RIGHT PROPER. BUT THAT *AIN'T* NO LIFE.

FATHER WAS MORE OF THE *ADVENTURIN'* TYPE.

WHAT *RIGHT* THINKING FOLK CALL A PIRATE.

LIKE ME.

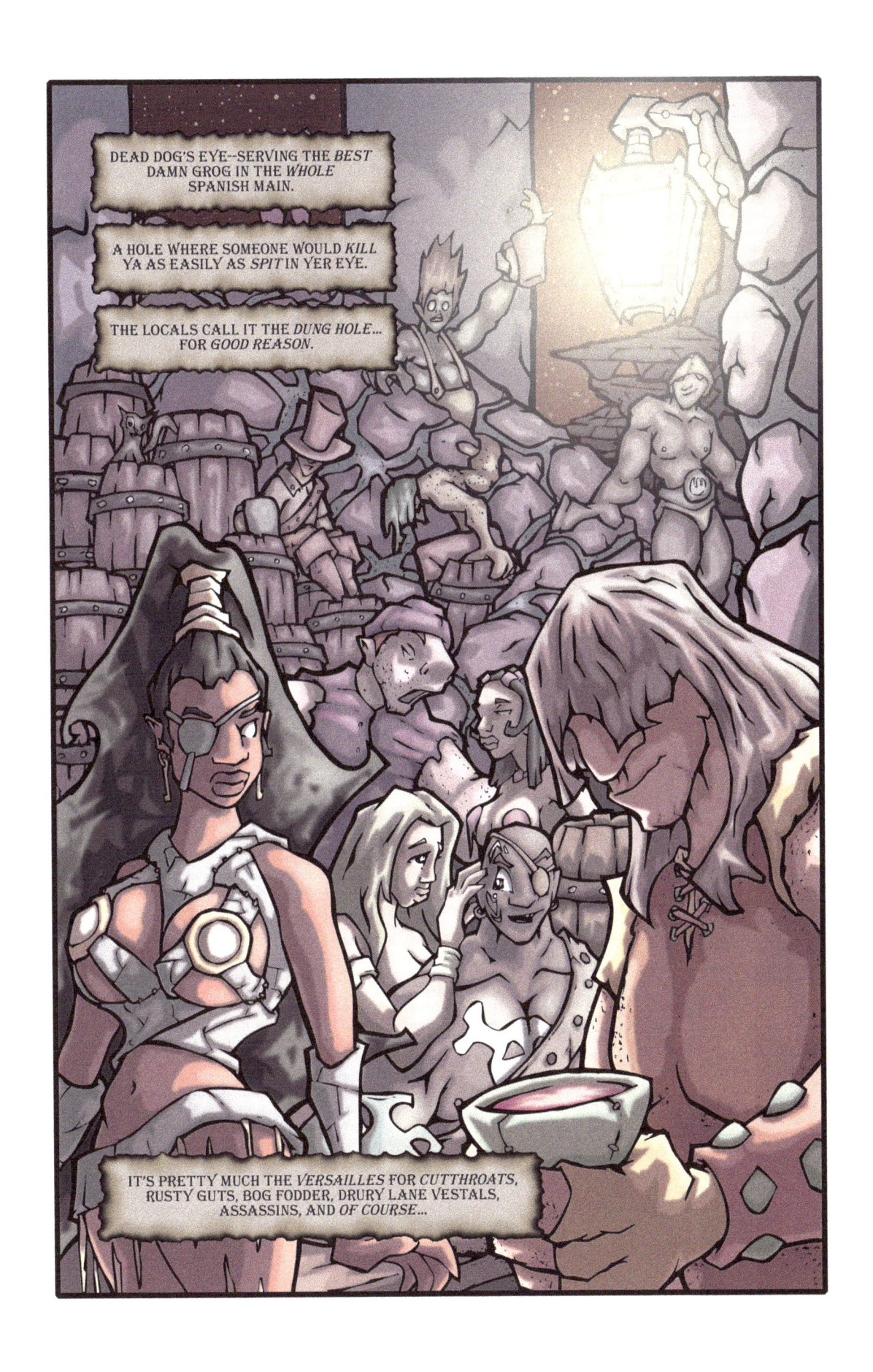

DEAD DOG'S EYE--SERVING THE *BEST* DAMN GROG IN THE *WHOLE* SPANISH MAIN.

A HOLE WHERE SOMEONE WOULD *KILL* YA AS EASILY AS *SPIT* IN YER EYE.

THE LOCALS CALL IT THE *DUNG HOLE*... FOR *GOOD REASON*.

IT'S PRETTY MUCH THE *VERSAILLES* FOR *CUTTHROATS*, RUSTY GUTS, BOG FODDER, DRURY LANE VESTALS, ASSASSINS, AND *OF COURSE*...

BOUNTY HUNTERS.
YOU AGAIN?
I THOUGH' I'D MAKE THIS INTERESTING?
TAKE YOU OUT WITH MY EYES CLOSED.
CAN WE DO THIS LATER?
I'M IN KIND OF A HURRY.
I DON'T SUPPOSE YOU MIGHT BE OPEN TO A BETTER OFFER?
IT'S GONNA COST YOU.
I TOLD HER MY STORY...LEAVIN' OUT ALL THE PRETTY PARTS— LIKE THE TRUTH.
LIFE IS EASIER WHEN YOU WORK ALONE, BUT TODAY IT'S SEEMIN' LIKE I COULD USE AN EXTRA SET.
BESIDES, THE MOMENT SHE WINKS AT ME SIDEWAYS, I'LL GUT HER LIKE A FISH.

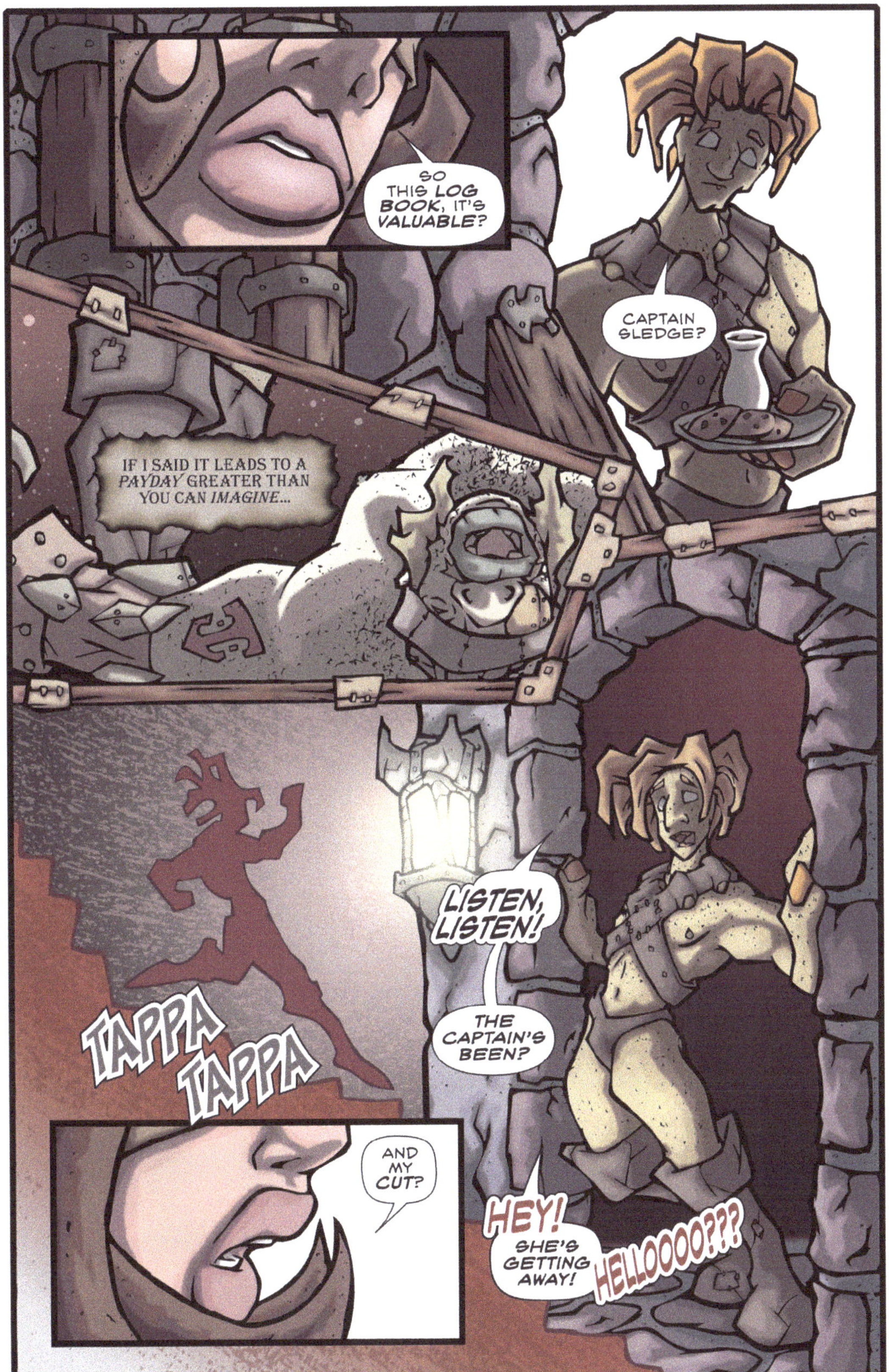
SO THIS LOG BOOK, IT'S VALUABLE?
CAPTAIN SLEDGE?
IF I SAID IT LEADS TO A PAYDAY GREATER THAN YOU CAN IMAGINE...
LISTEN, LISTEN!
THE CAPTAIN'S BEEN?
TAPPA TAPPA
AND MY CUT?
HEY!
SHE'S GETTING AWAY!
HELLOOOO???

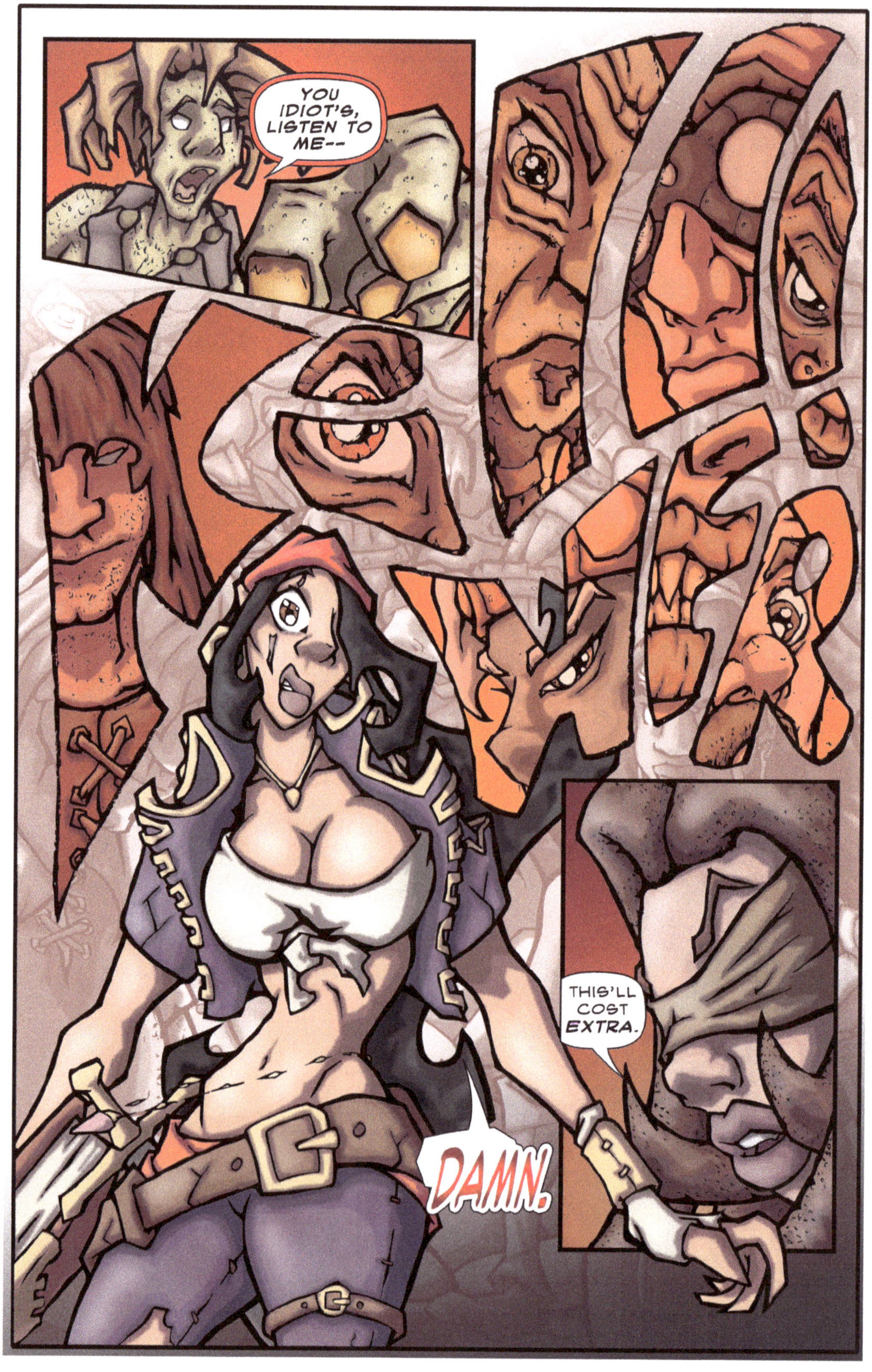

YOU IDIOT'S, LISTEN TO ME--
THIS'LL COST EXTRA.
DAMN.

BUT YOU MIGHT *QUALIFY* FOR THE *VOLUME DISCOUNT!*

CRUNK

SLAASASH

HURK
A PINT TO GO, PLEASE!
BLAM
C'MON, THERE'S STILL MORE!
JUST RUN FOR THE DOCKS!

AT THIS POINT IN MY STORY YOU MIGHT WONDER WHAT'S ALL THE FUSS OVER A RATTY, SODDEN *LOG BOOK*—'SPECIALLY ONE PENNED BY A HALF-LITERATE *IMBECILE* LIKE SLEDGE.

IT'S NOT THE BOOK ITSELF. IT'S NOT EVEN THE CRUDE MAPS POINTING TO *WORTHLESS* BOOTY PLUNDERED A LIFETIME AGO.

IT'S WHERE HE'S *BEEN*. *WHO* SLEDGE HAS *MET*.

IT'S THE *CLUES* IN BETWEEN THE LINES THAT WILL LEAD ME TO MY *PRIZE*.

AND *IF* THERE IS *TREASURE* TO BE FOUND ALONG THE WAY, SO BE IT.

BUT I *NEED* TO GET A *SHIP* FIRST.

SO WHAT'S YOUR PLAN?
IT'S A WORK IN PROGRESS, BUT IT ENDS UP WITH US TAKING OVER THAT SHIP.
THE ONE WITH THE ANGRY PIRATES?
THAT'S MILKING THE PIGEON!
AYE.
ELEGANT IN ITS SIMPLICITY.
LEMME MAP THIS OUT.
YOU DO REALIZE I'M BLIND.

VENGEANCE: A 14 GUN CORVETTE. ONCE THE *PRIDE* OF SA MAJESTÉ ROYALE, THE OLD SUN KING HIMSELF, *LOUIS XIV*, NOW *HAUNTS* THE WATERS OF THE CARIBBEAN UNDER A JOLLY ROGER.

NOW THIS PART OF THE STORY *AIN'T* FOR THE *FAINT OF HEART*. YOU KNOW BUCKETS OF *BLOOD*, SEVERED LIMBS AND THE LIKE.

As Madison jumps in the bay acting all helpless, I'll cut, slice and shoot my way down to the ship.

While them sea crabs ogle the damsel in distress, they *won't never* see my blade and pistol.

Least that's the *way* it works out in *my* head.

BOYS ---THERE'S AN EASY WAY, A HARD WAY---
---AND A WAY TO BECOME FILTHY RICH.
DID I MENTION THE HARD WAY?
FINE BY ME; JUST MORE CORPSES TO DUMP.
A LADY CAP'N?
WEEZ'LL BE THE LAUGHIN' STOCK OF THE SEVEN SEAS.
YOU SAID FILTHY RICH, RIGHT?

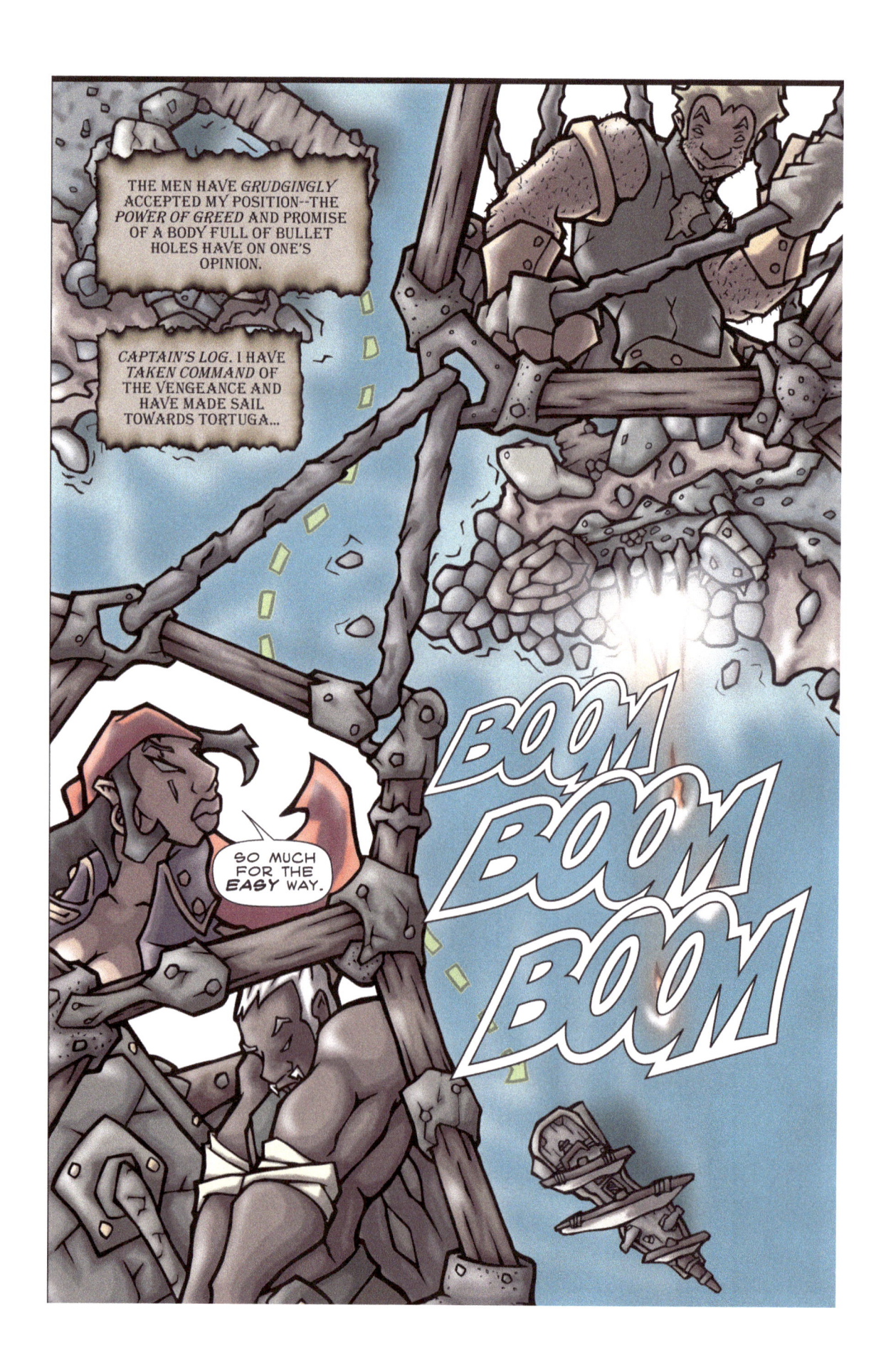

THE MEN HAVE *GRUDGINGLY* ACCEPTED MY POSITION--THE *POWER OF GREED* AND PROMISE OF A BODY FULL OF BULLET HOLES HAVE ON ONE'S OPINION.

CAPTAIN'S LOG. I HAVE *TAKEN COMMAND* OF THE VENGEANCE AND HAVE MADE SAIL TOWARDS TORTUGA...

SO MUCH FOR THE *EASY* WAY.

BOOM BOOM BOOM

THIS MIGHT BE A VERY SHORT ADVENTURE
I WON'T HAVE ME BOAT TURNED INTO NO HEN-FRIGATE!
BLOW IT TO BLOODY HELL!!!!
BLAMMM!
GET OFF YOUR ARSES!!
TIME TO EARN YOUR KEEP!

COME ABOUT AND BRING 'ER BROADSIDE!
LET'S SEND THAT ***BASTARD*** A LITTLE ***KISS!***
FIRE!!!!!!!!
BOOM

OH, BLAST.

KABOOM

HUZZAH!!!

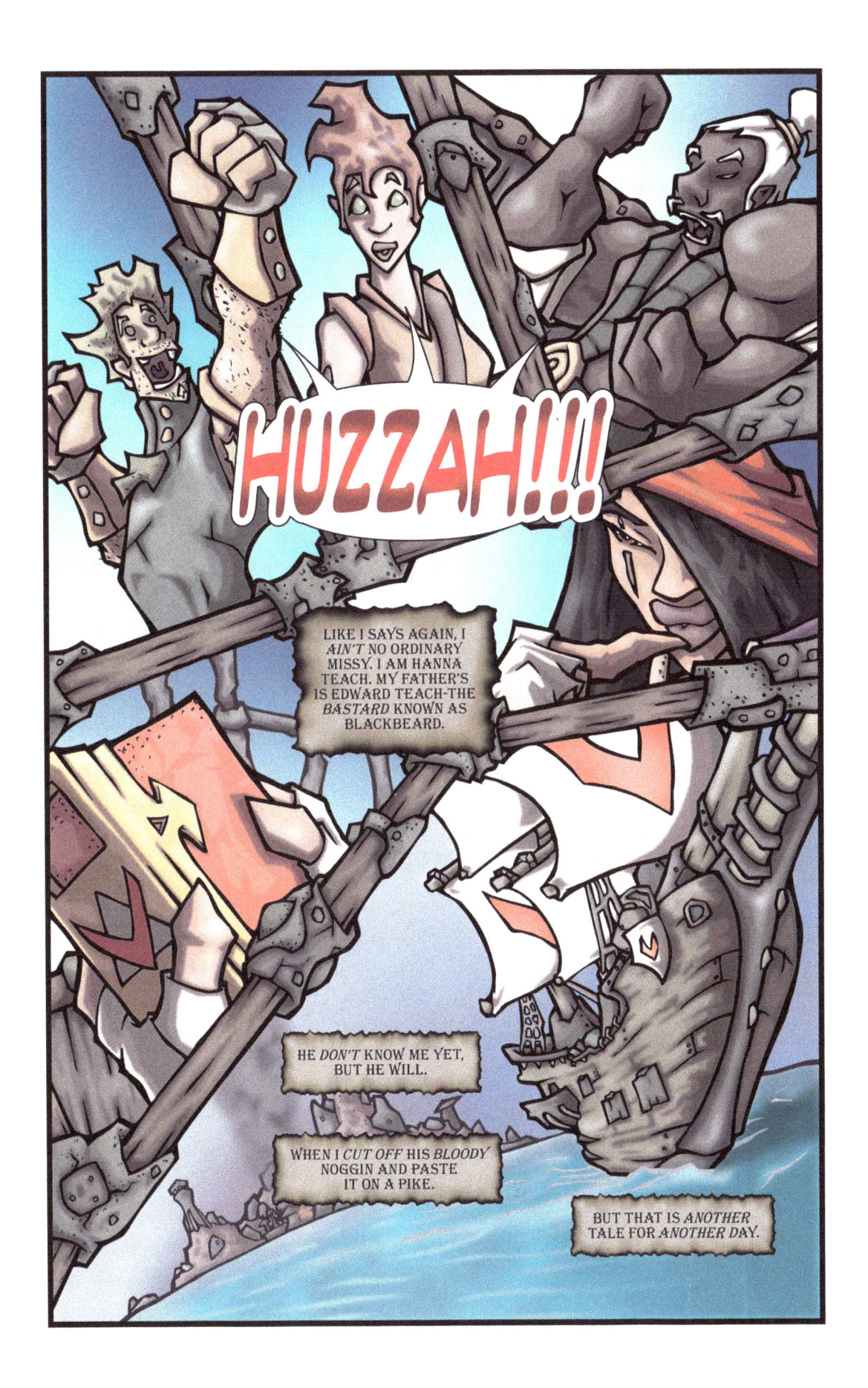

LIKE I SAYS AGAIN, I *AIN'T* NO ORDINARY MISSY. I AM HANNA TEACH. MY FATHER'S IS EDWARD TEACH—THE *BASTARD* KNOWN AS BLACKBEARD.

HE *DON'T* KNOW ME YET, BUT HE WILL.

WHEN I *CUT OFF* HIS *BLOODY* NOGGIN AND PASTE IT ON A PIKE.

BUT THAT IS *ANOTHER* TALE FOR *ANOTHER* DAY.

Chapter 2

BAYAMO

THERE ARE THINGS YOU NEVER PLAN ON.

RIGHT UP DANDIES CALL 'EM "UNINTENDED CONSEQUENCES."

ALL THEY IS ARE BARBARY BRULETS.

YA SET FIRE TO A SHIP AND POINT IT IN THE DIRECTION OF ANOTHER WITH THE HOPES OF BLOWIN' IT TO KINGDOM COME.

BUT CUZ OL' NEPTUNE CONTROLS THE FORTUNES OF THE SEA, SOMETIMES THERE'S...*UNINTENDED CONSEQUENCES*.

WAKEY WAKE MY LITTLE GRAVELINGS.
NOW THIS IS THE PART OF MY TALE YOU'LL THINK I'M PERFECTLY OFF ME HOOKS.
THREE DAYS AFTER WE BLEW UP FREE PORT TOWNSHIP.
THEY SAY DEAD MEN DON'T TELL NO TALES. WELL *THEY* NEVER MET OBEAHMANA.
THRUMM
THRUMM
BUM
THRUMM

FACT BE, AT THE TIME I HAD NO IDEA THAT THE BOUNTY HUNTER WITCH WANTED TO DRINK BLOOD FROM A SKULL.

MY BLOOD. MY SKULL.

"WAKEY WAKE AND WALK."

BUT SHE'S A COMIN'. AND SHE'S BRINGING SOME OLD FRIENDS.

THRUMM THRUMM

AHHHUUHHAHHH!

GOD, I *HATE* THE NIGHT.

THAT DREAM. THAT BLASTED DREAM ALWAYS RATTLES MY BONES.

STILL UNDER SAIL TOWARDS OFF THE COAST OF SOUTHWEST CUBA.

SOMEDAYS I FIGGER IT AIN'T ALL WORTH IT.

IF I JUST LIVE LIFE LIKE SOME CLUELESS BOUCAN RAIDIN' PORT ROYALE FOR PLUNDER, I CAN FILL THE HOLE THAT GNAWS IN MY GUT.

BLOODY HELL, I'M ACTIN' LIKE A FRENCHIFIED PETITE FILLE.

THEN I REMEMBER BLACKBEARD. I REMEMBER WHAT HE DONE.

AND THAT JUST *BOILS* MY BLOOD.

THIS BLOODY LOG GOES ON AND ON AND ON ABOUT A KEYE.

CALLS IT "THE BYOOTEEFUL CIRCLE."

SOUNDS LIKE ANOTHER PIRATE FAIRYTALE. BUT THAT BASTARD SAILED WITH BLACKBEARD IN THE OLD DAYS. AND HIS MAPS CAN BRING ME ONE STEP CLOSER.

SLEDGE WEREN'T NO POET, BUT HE KNOWS THE CARIBBEAN.

IF I FIND THAT KEY... *I WILL FIND HIM.*

MIGGY SAYS YOU CHANGED COURSE. SAYS WERE HEADIN' FOR CUBA.
MIGGY'S AN IDIOT.
HE GOSSIPS LIKE AN OLD WOMAN. HE'S GONNA FIND HIMSELF KEELHAULED IF HE DON'T SHUT HIS TRAP.
HEY, I MAY BE BLIND... BUT I'M NOT STUPID!
CUBA'S A REAL BAD IDEA.
MAYBE SO. BUT IT'S MY IDEA. AND LAST I CHECKED, I WAS CAPTAIN OF THIS TUG.

YOU BEST TREAD CAREFULLY. THIS IS THE KINDA SLAG THAT GETS YOU KILLED.
WORSE YET...GETS *ME* KILLED.
IS THAT A THREAT?
THE BLOODY ROYAL LEATHERNECKERS ARE CAMPED IN HAVANA JUST WAITIN' FOR RATS LIKE US TO BLUNDER INTO THEIR BACKYARD.
AND YOU KNOW THIS HOW?
WHOD'YA THINK HIRED ME TO FIND YOU?
AND I AIN'T THE ONLY ONE.
YOUR LUST FOR REVENGE IS GONNA TAKE A BITE OUT OF MY PROFITS.
MY SHIP. MY WAY. NOTHIN'S STOPPIN' YOU FROM JUMPIN' IN THE BRINY AND LEAVING OUR EMPLOY.

LAND HO!!!
CUBA OFF THE PORT BOW.
I'M TELLIN' YOU NOW.
THIS AIN'T GONNA END WELL.
I GOT NO DESIRE TO SWING FROM THE GALLOWS... OR WORSE.
TELL ME SOMETHING I DON'T KNOW.

MADISON FORGETS THIS AIN'T ABOUT WRITIN' OUR NAMES NEXT TO MORGAN, KIDD AND ROBERTS.

AND THE CREW HAS TO KEEP THINKIN' THERE'S TREASURE AT THE END OF THIS RAINBOW.

THERE'S A KEY HERE.

SLEDGE WAS A LOT OF THINGS.

A BACON-FACED THIEF, A CUTTHROAT BILGESCRAPER...BUT MOST ESPECIALLY HE WAS A GREEDY BASTARD.

AND HE WEREN'T SMART ENOUGH TO PLANT A RUSE

SO IF HIS DAMN LOG BOOK SAYS THERE'S A KEY. THERE'S A KEY.

SO I SAY TO 'IM, 'E'S KICKED THE BUCKET, SHUFFLED OFF THE MORTAL COIL, RUN DOWN THE CURTAIN AND JOINED THE CHOIR INVISIBLE. *THIS* IS AN *EX*-PARROT.

WAS IT THE NORWEGIAN BLUE?

I HEAR IT HAS LOVELY PLUMAGE.

TALK TO EVERY SLAG, COURTESAN, PONGO AND GADFLY.
WE FIND THE KEY.
WE FIND THE PRIZE.
SUCH DANGEROUS QUESTIONS.
NO KEY. WANNA BUY A MONKEY?
NO SABE.
ENCONTRE O HOMEM DE QUEM O DEUS NÃO GOSTA E VOCÊ ENCONTRA A CHAVE.*
* PORTUGUESE TRANSLATION: FIND THE MAN WHOM THE LORD FROWNS UPON AND YOU FIND THE KEY.
BUGGER OFF.

URRRRRRPPP!
HUH?
BUY ME A PINT. MAYBE I KNOW A THING OR TWO.
WHY SHOULD I TELLS YOU ANYT'ING?
THIS ISLAND HOLDS MANY SECRETS.
A MAN WHO TURNS LEAD TO GOLD HAS THE KEY TO IMMORTAL LIFE.
I KNOWS A BLOKE, WHO KNOWS A BLOKE.

OH'NO NO NO!
EL MONSTRUO WHO PISSES CON EL DIABLO.
THERE BE THINGS BETTER NOT KNOWN.
YOU GOT THE KEY TO MY HEART, LOVER.
WHEN IS A KEY NOT A KEY, BUT STILL IS A KEY?
GRUMM DLL UGGA PHLOOF!
THERE'S A LOT UNSPOKEN HERE. SOMETHIN'S MAKIN' THE LOCALS VERY EDGY.
'S OFF THE SOUTHERN TIP OF FLORIDA.

AND THE SQUIDGIER THEY GET, MEANS THE CLOSER I AM.

DA KEY ONLY BRINGS DEATH.

JUS' GET IN YER SHIP AN' SAIL AWAY.

MEOW?

GRUUMMPH.

GO UP DA HILL, YOU NEVER COME DOWN.

I AM ZIGIMUND, ASSISTANT TO MIJNHEER VANDER KEYE.

PERHAPS I CAN BE OF SERVICE TO YOU?

ZA MASTER OF ZA HOUSE IS OVERSEAS.

WHEN IS A KEY NOT A KEY, BUT STILL A KEY?!

I CAN SEE WHY THE PLACE SPOOKS THE LOCALS.
A REGULAR RAT TRAP WITH GADGETS AND THINGAMAJIGS...AND THAT REAL CREEPY WALKIN' SHAB-RAG.
I'M HERE FOR A KEY. AND BY HOOK OR BY CROOK I MEANS TO LEAVE WITH IT.
IF YOU WISH A KEY, YOU FIRST NEED TO KNOW WHAT IT UNLOCKS.
THEN YOU ENGAGE A LOCKSMITH, NOT A TINKER.
VE MAKE MANY T'INGS HERE, BUT I KNOW OF NO KEY.
MY BOOK SAYS DIFF'RENT.
DON'T BELIEVE EVERYTHING YOU READ.

THE DUTCHMAN IS LYING. WE'LL JUST SEE IF I BE A BIT MORE PERSUASIVE NEXT TIME.

I'M SORRY, BUT YOU CAME A LONG WAY FOR NOTHING.

SHE'S HERE.

SHE'S NOT A DREAM...

AND WHEN YOU KNOW WHAT IT UNLOCKS, WILL YOU REALLY WANT TO OPEN THE DOOR?
MIJNHEER, WHAT DO WISH ME TO DO?
SHE MOST DEFINITELY WILL RETURN WITH WHAT I ASSUME WILL BE A MOST CONVINCING DISPLAY OF FORCE.
MAYBE WE JUST GRANT HER DEAREST WISH AND GIVE HER THE DAMN THING--THE GOOD IT EVER DID ME.

I LOOK INTO THE FACES OF THE CREW AND LIE RIGHT TO THEIR GOBS.

MEBBE IT JUS' AIN'T DERE. MEBBE DERE IS NO KEY.

IT'S THERE ALRIGHT. AND IF I GOTTA SLICE THAT DIKE-PLUGGER AND TEAR THE WHOLE DAMN PLACE APART. I'LL FIND IT.

"BOYS, THIS IS WHY YOU SIGNED ON TO THIS LITTLE ADVENTURE."

"YEP, THEY MIGHT WELL DIE, BUT IF THAT'S THE PRICE..."

"S'LONG AS THERE IS A BIT O' BOOTY AT THE END OF THE DAY, I'LL KILL ME OWN GRAN'MAMA."

"I'LL LET GOD OR OL' NICK JUDGE ME WHEN THE TIME COMES."

"SO D'YA WANNA GET RICH OR NOT?"

"I FEEL THE BAYAMO WIND. IT'LL HAVE QUITE A BITE."

"CAN'T YOU TELL ME WHY THIS DAMN KEY IS SO IMPORTANT?"

HIC!

SHE WOULDN'T UNDERSTAND

SHE AIN'T NEVER SEEN HER MOTHER DEFILED.

HERE'S TO THE GIRL WITH A PAIR OF BLUE EYES.

HERE'S TO THE CHARMER WHOSE DIMPLES WE PRIZE. NOW TO THE DAMSEL WITH NONE.

NOW TO THE NYMPH WITH BUT ONE.

NEVER WATCHED HER MOTHER, TORTURED BY SHAME, SLIP ON A NEWGATE NECKTIE.

SHE'S NEVER SEEN THE DEVIL.

LET THE TOAST PASS, DRINK TO THE...

I HAVE.

TIME TO PLAY MY BEASTIES, MY BEAUTIES.

LASS...
I GOTTA STOP BOOZIN' ON WEDNESDAYS.
AND BY GOD'S HOOKS I 'M GONNA SEND THAT SLAG BACK TO HELL.
BRING ME THE HEAD OF BLACKBEARD'S DAUGHTER!

Chapter 3

nepo
colors

MAMA ONCE ME TOLD THERE AIN'T NOTHING WORTH LOSIN' YOUR HEAD OVER.

SHE ALSO THE ONLY THING THAT FALLS FROM THE SKY IS RAIN AND BIRD TURD.

MAMA HAD NO CLUE 'BOUT THE WORLD.

BUT IN DEFENSE OF MAMA'S WISDOM, IN ALL MY LIVIN', THIS IS THE *FIRST* HEADLESS BEAU-NASTY I'VE SEEN SPILL FROM THE HEAVENS.

GOD'S HOOKS!

THIS JUST CAN'T BE A GOOD THING.

EVEN KING GEORGIE-PORGIE'S FINEST MAN-O'WAR CAN'T ESCAPE THE SCOURGE OF THE BILGE *RAT*.

THEY FEED OFF THE SEWERY SLOP OF RANCID WATER AND TACK IN THE DARKEST SHAB-RAG CRITCH OF THE SHIP. AND ALL THE SCRUBBIN' AND SWABBIN' MAKES NO NEVER MIND.

SOONER OR LATER THEY *PUKE* TO THE SURFACE AND FOUL THE WHOLE SHIP.

GO ME LOVELY LOVELIES. I NEEDS ME THE BEATIN' HEART OF BLACKYBEARD'S SIRE.

MAKE THEM ALL...

DIE

THE *ONLY* CURE FOR BILGE RATS IS JUST KILL'EM ON SITE.

BUT THE PROBLEM WITH THEM RATS IS YOU KILLS ONE AND THERE'S TEN TO TAKE ITS PLACE.

A PLAGUE OF *RATS*.

I THINKS I SOILED MESELF.

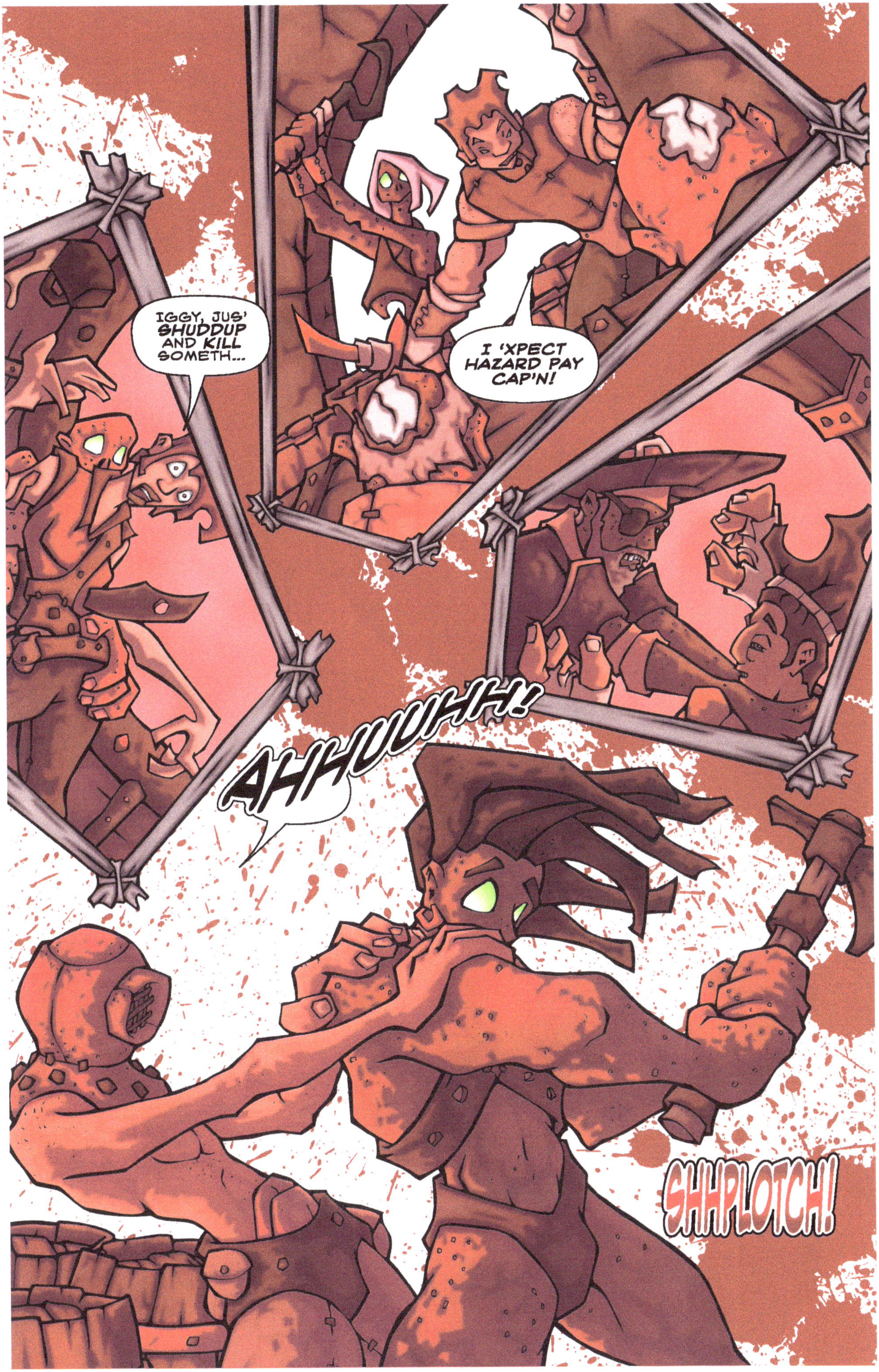
IGGY, JUS' SHUDDUP AND KILL SOMETH...
I 'XPECT HAZARD PAY CAP'N!
AHHUUUHH!
SHHPLOTCH!

AAAAAAAAAAAHHHHHHHHHHH!
I FEEL A SPLITTIN' HEADACHE COMING ON.
BLOODY ZOMBIES, RUINING A PERFECTLY GOOD BLOODY DAY.
KROGGKKK!

AT THIS POINT IN MY TALE, YOU'RE PROBABLY THINKIN' THAT I'M YANKIN' YOUR YARDARM.
NO ONE CAN RAISE THE DEAD. NONE BUT THE HEAVENLY HOST HIMSELF.
BUT YOU'LL BE BEST OFF TO LEARN, THAT SOMETIMES HELL BOILS OVER.
THWOK

THERE'S AN OLD SONG I REMEMBER: "YOU CAN BLOW OUT A CANDLE.

THWACK

BUT YOU CAN'T BLOW OUT A FIRE.

ONCE THE FLAMES BEGIN TO CATCH, THE WIND WILL BLOW IT HIGHER."

AND WE'RE LOOKING DOWN THE MAW OF A BUGGER-ALL GALE!

SWASH

AND LO SAYETH THE QUEEN OF HEARTS...

OFF!

OFF WITH THEIR HEADS!

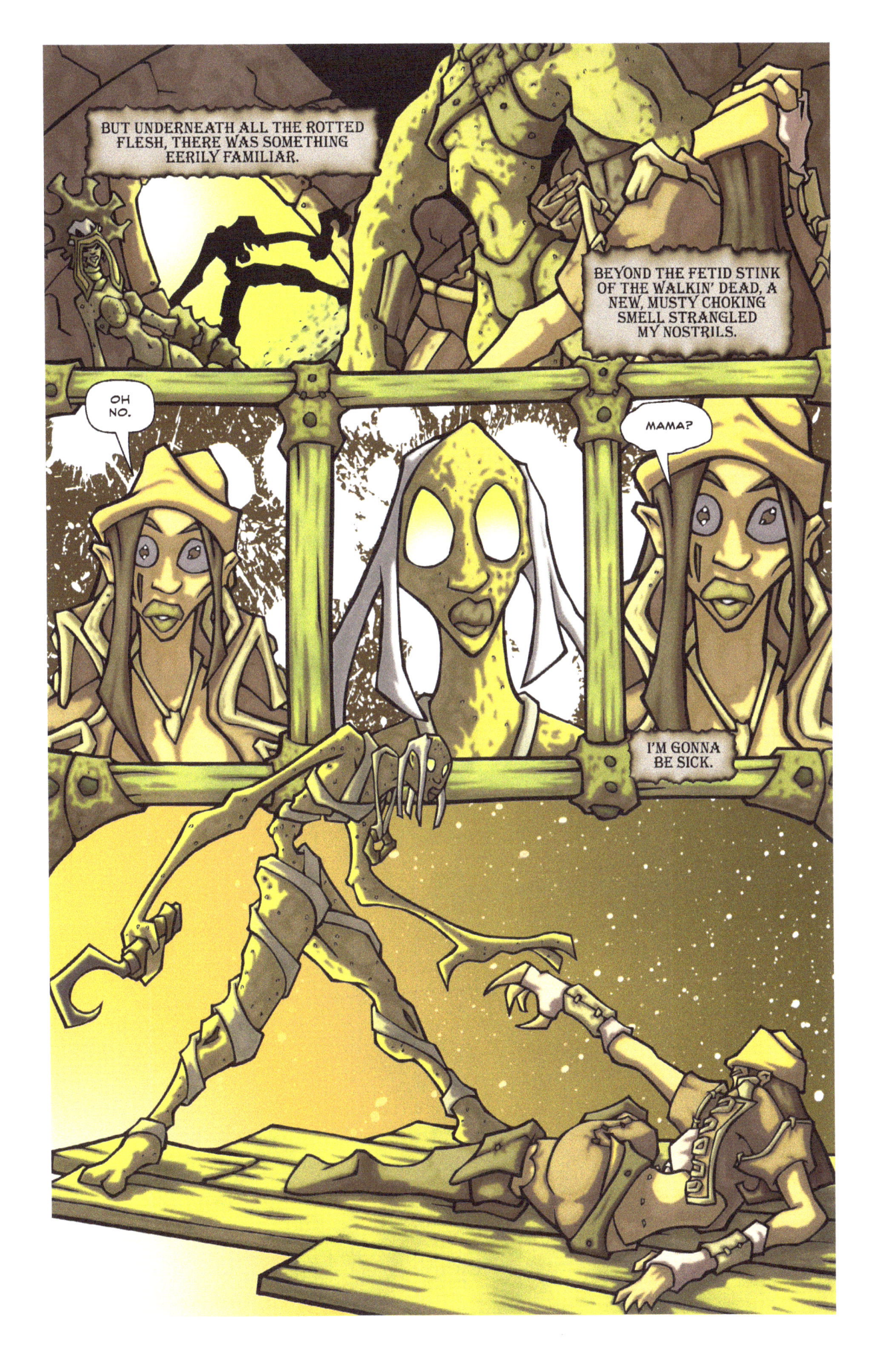

BUT UNDERNEATH ALL THE ROTTED FLESH, THERE WAS SOMETHING EERILY FAMILIAR.

BEYOND THE FETID STINK OF THE WALKIN' DEAD, A NEW, MUSTY CHOKING SMELL STRANGLED MY NOSTRILS.

OH NO.

MAMA?

I'M GONNA BE SICK.

GEE-VUSH KISH, SHWEETING! GEEVUSH BOOOKHH!
SLEDGE?
THEY'LL LET ANY OLD SLAG OUTTA HELL THESE DAYS.
Klank
AND I TOLD YOU BEFORE...
NEVER CALL ME SWEET THING!

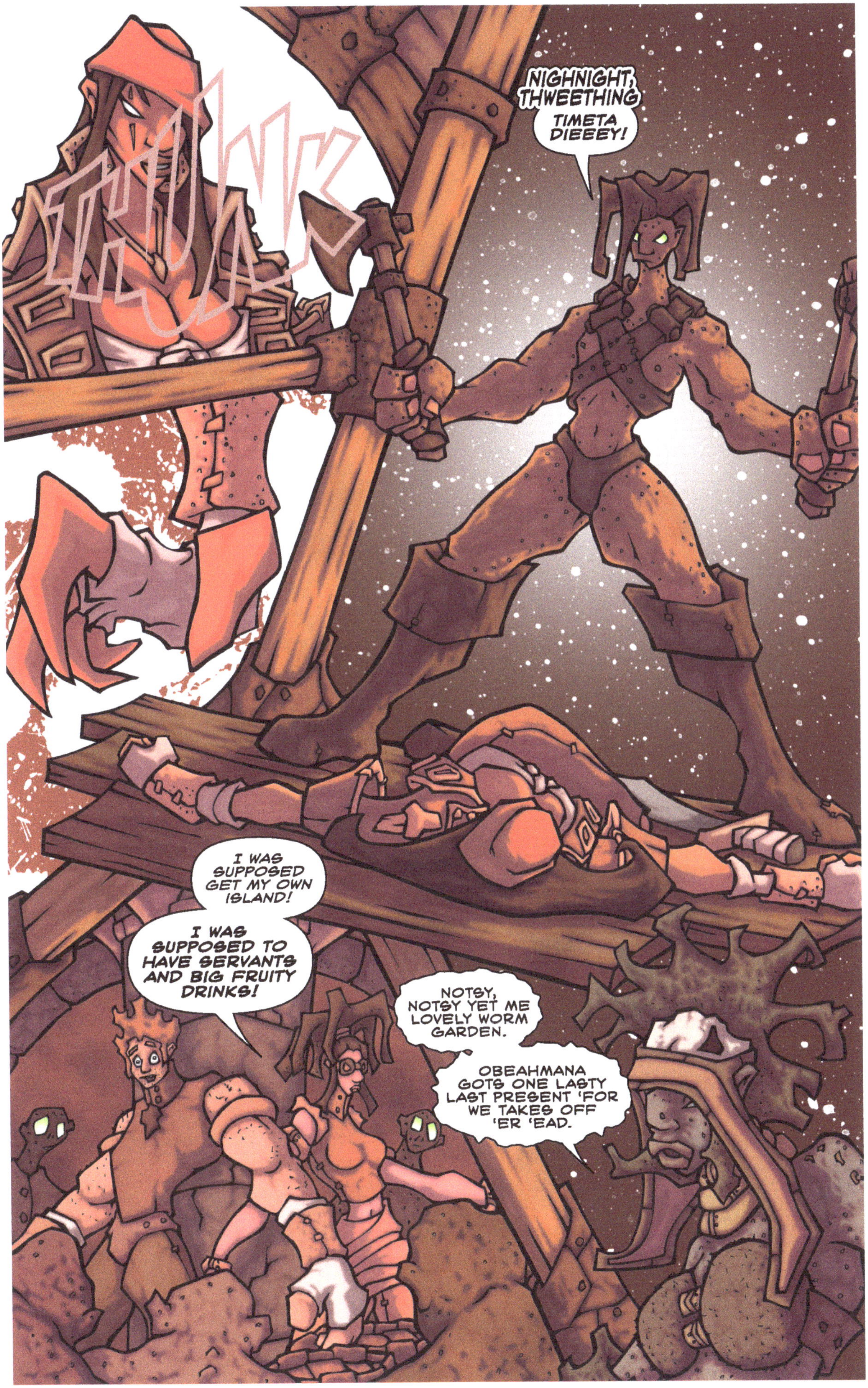
THUNK
NIGHNIGHT, THWEETHING
TIMETA DIEEEY!
I WAS SUPPOSED GET MY OWN ISLAND!
I WAS SUPPOSED TO HAVE SERVANTS AND BIG FRUITY DRINKS!
NOTSY, NOTSY YET ME LOVELY WORM GARDEN.
OBEAHMANA GOTS ONE LASTY LAST PRESENT 'FOR WE TAKES OFF 'ER 'EAD.

IT ALL CAME BACK.

KNIFIN' THROUGH ME LIKE DROWNIN' IN THE ARCTIC.

IT WAS THE NIGHTMARE... BUT I WASN'T ASLEEP.

HOW THE BASTARD BLACKBEARD TOOK UNWELCOME LIBERTIES WITH MAMA.

HOW HE PAID NO NEVER MIND THAT I WAS IN THE ROOM.

HOW HE CAME BACK AGAIN AND AGAIN; GIVIN' US NO MORE REGARD THAN THE DOG CRAP ON THE BOTTOM OF HIS BOOT.

HOW HE PUSHED HER TO THE GREAT BEYOND.

HOW HELPLESS I WAS.

I AM.

IT ALL CAME BACK.

AND NONE OF IT SEEMED TO MATTER A DAMN BIT.

BLACKBEARD MAY NOT HAVE SLIPPED THE NOOSE ROUND HER NECK, BUT HE KILLED HER ALL THE SAME.

RIGHTY RIGHT MAMA.

LI'L GIRL 'AS BEEN VERY VERY BAD.

YOU MUST PUNISH HER. **KILL HER!**

THRUMM THRUMM THRUMM THRUMM

'AN... NA

SACRIFICE.

NO NOT AGAIN! MAMA...MAMA.... MAMA-DALLION?

BEAUTIFUL CIRCLE?

HE WILL PAY.

THAT SON OF A WHORE WILL *BEG* ME TO KILL HIM.

SOMEWAY, SOMEHOW, HE WILL *FEEL* MAMA'S SACRIFICE.

GTHLACK!

I SWEAR IT.

SOMEBODY CALL FOR THE CAVALRY?
SMASH
THE MEDALLION. IT'S THE KEY. *A BEAUTIFUL CIRCLE*. THAT'S WHAT SLEDGE WROTE.
I'VE BEEN A BLEEDING CULLY. I NEEDED TO GET MY GRUBBY MITTS ON THE *DAMNED* THING SO BAD THAT I DAMNED MY MAMA.
OH, DONCHA GO GOIN' MAKIN' OLD OBEAHMANA MADSY ANGRY LIKE.
WONCHA DIE LIKE A GOODY-GOOD GIRL?
NAH, IT WASN'T ME WHO DAMNED MAMA. IT WAS THAT BUCK-FITCH HAG.
SCHEPSEL, TAKE HER.
I'LL JUST HAVE ME A LITTLE CHAT WITH THIS LOT IN A LANGUAGE THEY'LL UNDERSTAND.
RING AROUND THE ROSIE, POCKET FULL OF POSIES...

ASHES, ASHES, THEY ALL FALL DOWN!
FLOOM!
"WITHIN THESE FIRES ARE THE SPIRITS; EACH IS SWATHED BY THAT WHEREWITH HE IS ENKINDLED."
WHAT'S THE MATTER, NOT UP ON YOUR DANTE?
FINE, LET ME GIVE THE SHORT VERSION.
CRACKLE
VEEL 'OT.

I KNOW I'M S'POSED TO FEEL SOMETHING FOR THOSE BLASTED DOG-ENDS AND MONGRELS WHICH DONE GOT THEMSELVES KILLED.

A PIRATE'S LIFE AIN'T FOR FOPS AND DANDIES AND THEY KNEW THE RISKS.

DAMN FOOLS.

DAMN THEM.

DAMN IT ALL TO HELL. IT WASN'T S'POSED TO BE LIKE THIS.

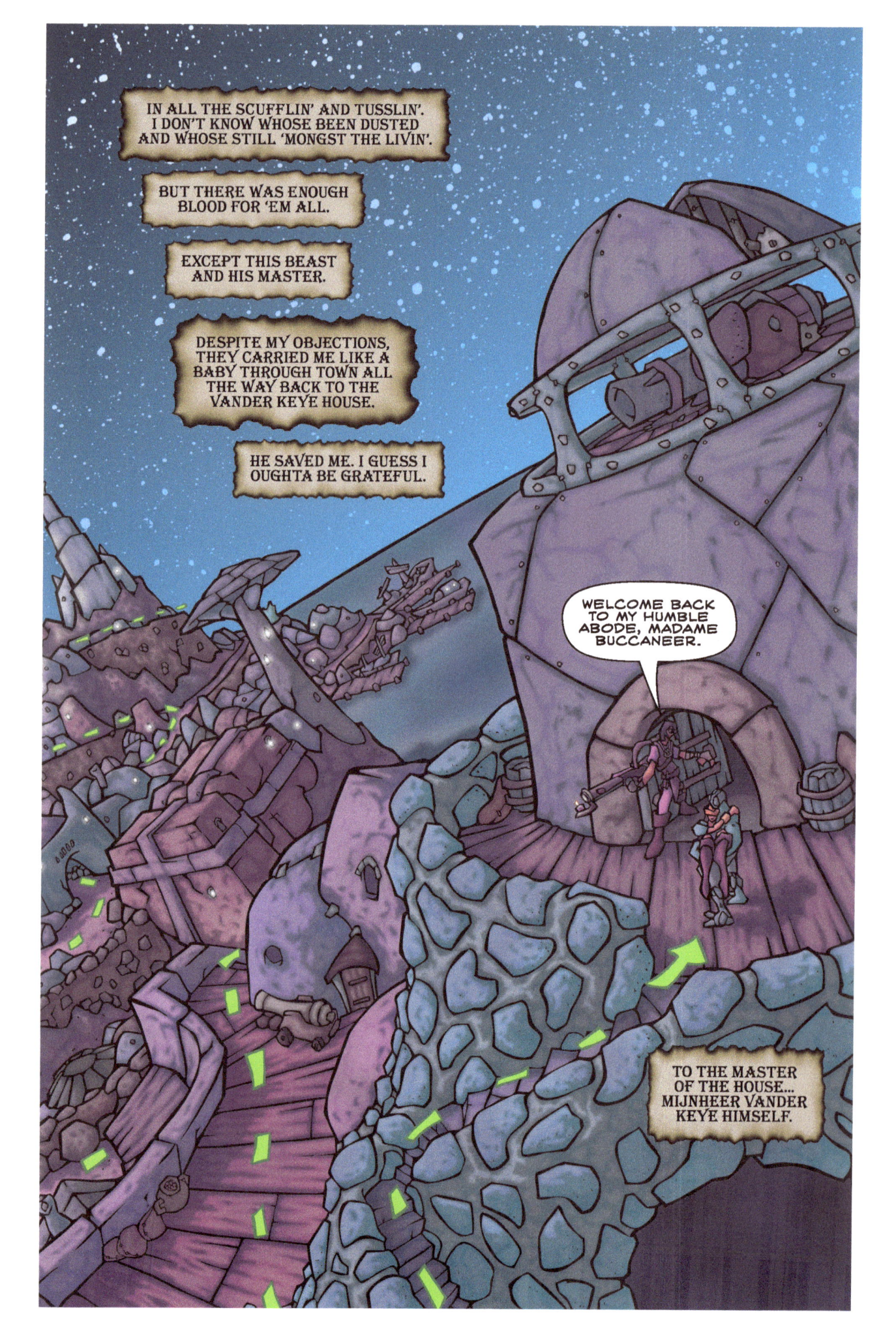

IN ALL THE SCUFFLIN' AND TUSSLIN'. I DON'T KNOW WHOSE BEEN DUSTED AND WHOSE STILL 'MONGST THE LIVIN'.

BUT THERE WAS ENOUGH BLOOD FOR 'EM ALL.

EXCEPT THIS BEAST AND HIS MASTER.

DESPITE MY OBJECTIONS, THEY CARRIED ME LIKE A BABY THROUGH TOWN ALL THE WAY BACK TO THE VANDER KEYE HOUSE.

HE SAVED ME. I GUESS I OUGHTA BE GRATEFUL.

"WELCOME BACK TO MY HUMBLE ABODE, MADAME BUCCANEER."

TO THE MASTER OF THE HOUSE... MIJNHEER VANDER KEYE HIMSELF.

YOU ARE NOT THE MOST SUBTLE OF PIRATES, MY DEAR SISTER.
MAMA'S DEAD... AGAIN.
AND SO SHALL...
SISTER?
AYE, ANOTHER PRODUCT OF THE LOINS OF EDWARD TEACH.
I AM EDWARD VANDER KEYE OR EDWARD TEACH, JR.
IF YOU CHOOSE TO INSULT ME.
RRRRRRRRRUMMMMMBLE
I COULDA LEFT YOU WITH THE VOODOO WITCH.
BESIDES, WE'RE FAMILY.
DO YOU THINK MY TRUST COMES THAT EASY?
IT'S NOT SAFE HERE. WE NEED TO GET OFF THE ISLAND.

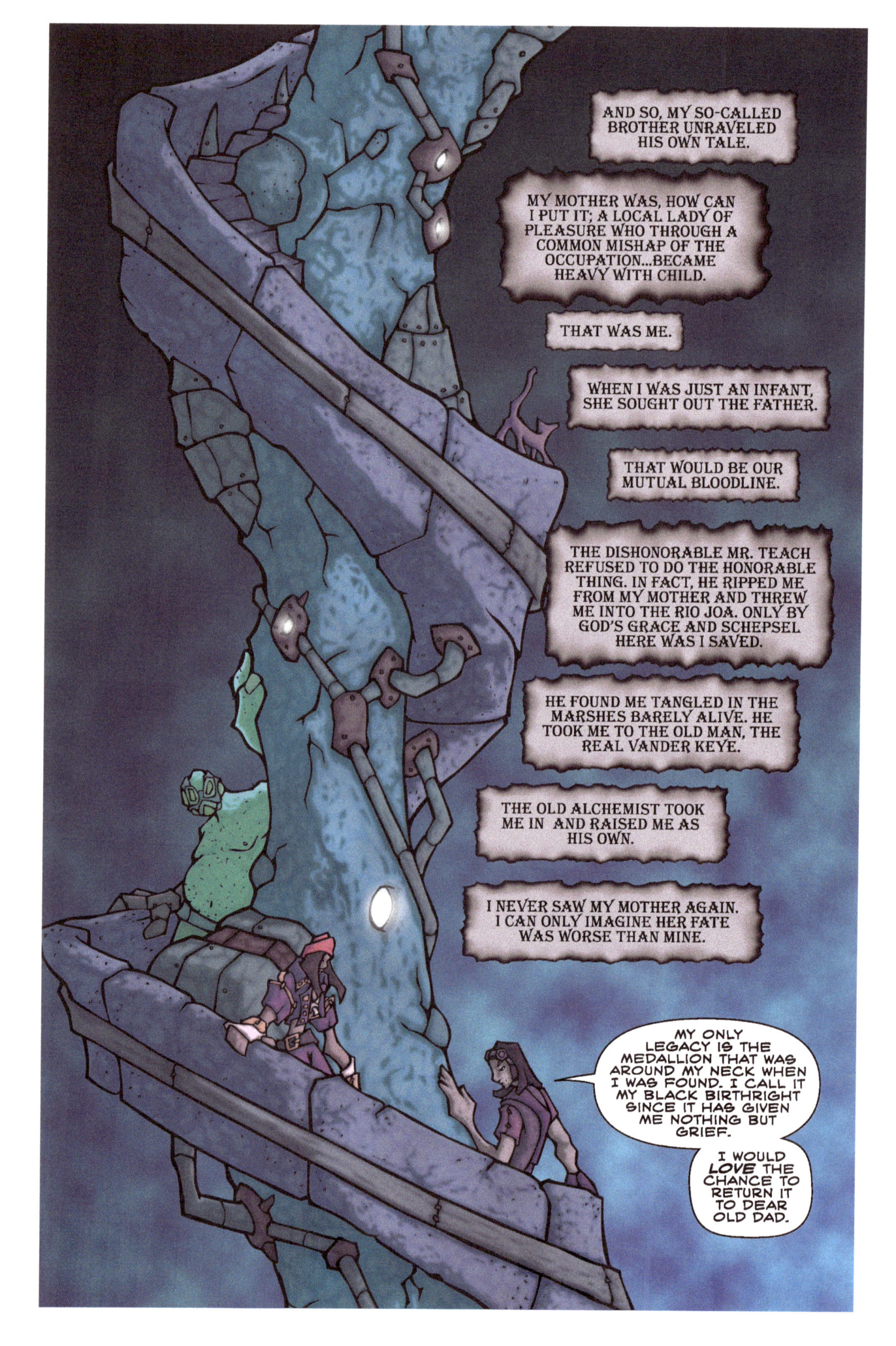

AND SO, MY SO-CALLED BROTHER UNRAVELED HIS OWN TALE.

MY MOTHER WAS, HOW CAN I PUT IT; A LOCAL LADY OF PLEASURE WHO THROUGH A COMMON MISHAP OF THE OCCUPATION...BECAME HEAVY WITH CHILD.

THAT WAS ME.

WHEN I WAS JUST AN INFANT, SHE SOUGHT OUT THE FATHER.

THAT WOULD BE OUR MUTUAL BLOODLINE.

THE DISHONORABLE MR. TEACH REFUSED TO DO THE HONORABLE THING. IN FACT, HE RIPPED ME FROM MY MOTHER AND THREW ME INTO THE RIO JOA. ONLY BY GOD'S GRACE AND SCHEPSEL HERE WAS I SAVED.

HE FOUND ME TANGLED IN THE MARSHES BARELY ALIVE. HE TOOK ME TO THE OLD MAN, THE REAL VANDER KEYE.

THE OLD ALCHEMIST TOOK ME IN AND RAISED ME AS HIS OWN.

I NEVER SAW MY MOTHER AGAIN. I CAN ONLY IMAGINE HER FATE WAS WORSE THAN MINE.

MY ONLY LEGACY IS THE MEDALLION THAT WAS AROUND MY NECK WHEN I WAS FOUND. I CALL IT MY BLACK BIRTHRIGHT SINCE IT HAS GIVEN ME NOTHING BUT GRIEF.

I WOULD *LOVE* THE CHANCE TO RETURN IT TO DEAR OLD DAD.

I'VE HEARD ME LOTS OF SOB STORIES, SO A FEW SNIFFLES AND 'AW SHUCKS DON'T MAKE IT ANY MORE TRUE.

AND PEOPLE DON'T FALL OUT OF THE SKY AND ANNOUNCE THEY'RE KIN.

BUT IF HE CAN GET ME ONE STEP CLOSER TO BLACKBEARD THEN SO BE IT.

AND HE KNEW 'BOUT THE KEY-THAT MEDALLION-WITHOUT ME ASKIN'.

A CIRCULAR MEDALLION?

LEMME SEE IT.

A MATCH AS PERFECT AS THE ACE OF SPADES AND HIS DARK SUITED QUEEN.

IT'S TRUE. IT'S ALL *BLOODY* TRUE. WE'RE FAMILY!

I'VE *WAITED* AND HOPED FOR THIS DAY.

THEN IT BEGAN TO HAPPEN.

IT STARTED WITH THAT DIZZYING FEELIN' YOU GET WHEN PUT OUT TO SEA FOR THE FIRST TIME.

MY WHOLE BODY BUZZED AND THEN THE MEDALLION FLEW FROM MY HANDS.

IT SNABBLED AND CANOODLED WITH ME BROTHER'S MEDALLION. IT HUNG IN THE AIR IN THE SAME WAY ANCHORS DON'T.

ANNE'S FAN!

MMMMM?

CRIKEY.... IT'S A MAP.

NOT JUST A MAP. IT'S *THE* MAP.

IT'S WHERE WE'LL FIND *HIM!*

THIS WAS S'POSED TO BE ONE THEM MOMENTS YOU SIT BACK AND CROW.

BUT LIKE MOST OF THIS ADVENTURE, THINGS WENT ALL TAILS AND TURDS.

D'YOU HEAR SOMETHING?

OH MY WICKED WICKED WANDERERS. OBEAHMANA IS AWFULLY CRISSLY-CROSS AND PLAYTIME IS AT A FINISHED END.

Chapter 4

SOMEWHERE OFF THE OUTER BANK ISLANDS OF THE BRITISH COLONY OF NORTH CAROLINA.

NO ONE SAID NUTHIN' 'BOUT ZOMBIES.

SORRY 'BOUT THAT IGGY.

I'VE GOT ENOUGH PROBLEMS WITHOUT YOU GOING ALL UNDEAD ON ME.

THE PATRON SAINT OF REVENGE

GIVE HER A LITTLE PUSH.

GIVE A LITTLE PROD.

KEEP HER GOIN' IN CIRCLES. BUT NO BLOODY WALKIN' CORPSES.

FWWWZZZzzz

LOOKY WHAT I CAUGHT!
IT'LL LOOK LOVELY STUFFED AND MOUNTED ON ME WALL.

"WELCOME ABOARD THE QUEEN ANNE'S REVENGE.

THERE'S DANCING ON THE LIDO DECK, AND TONIGHT'S MENU FEATURES...

YOU."

"YOU'RE ABOUT TO FEEL LIKE A STEAK, FROM THE COW'S POINT OF VIEW."

"WE'LL HAVE NONE OF THAT, LASS."

YOU BASTARD!
YOU NEARLY GOT ME KILLED!
HAZARD OF YOUR PROFESSION I'M AFRAID.
I THOUGHT YOU WOULD BE A MORE VALUABLE ASSET, LADY MADISON. OBVIOUSLY THIS WAS A MISJUDGMENT.
SHE'S STILL COMIN'.
SHE'S STILL ALIVE AND GONNA CARVE YOU LIKE A CHRISTMAS GOOSE!
HA HEH HAH!
GLORIOUS!
BIND HER. GAG HER AND THROW HER IN THE HOLD.
CHANGE OF PLANS MR. CLAY.
COME ABOUT AND HEAD FOR HOME.

OH, MY PRETTY, PRETTY BIRD.
YOU HAVE BEEN A STICKY THORN IN OL' OBEAHMANA'S SIDE.
"STORIES OF FINDING BURIED TREASURE ARE ALL SHITE. PIRATE REALITIES END IN ONE OF THREE WAYS.
I HAPPY TO BE MORE THAN THAT.
GULLEYED LIKE COTSWOLD LION; ON THE BUSINESS END OF A HANGMAN'S NOOSE; OR FIDDLIN' A REQUIEM WITH DAVY JONES. THEY NEVER END WELL FOR THE PIRATE."
"YOU HAVE BEEN A LUCKY, LUCKY GIRL, BUT NOW WE FINISH THINGS OURSELVES. NO MORE TRICKSY TRICKS."
BETTY LUCKY THAN DEAD.
NO BETTER TIME THAN TO BREAK WITH TRADITION.
GROOOOOOFFF
LUCK'S FICKLE FUNNY, GIRLIE.
IT CHANGES AT A MOMENTS.

NO, SCHEPSEL! NO!
I DUNNO HOW, BUT I SAW *LOVE* IN THAT BEAST'S FACE.
HE DIDN'T SHOVE ME OVER FOR ANY LOVE OF ME. IT WAS EDDIE.
EDDIE WAS HIS BROTHER, HIS FATHER, HIS SON, HIS FRIEND.
NO NO NO NO! NO!
THAT MONSTER WAS SACRIFICING HISSELF, SO EDDIE COULD ESCAPE.

KILLS DEM ALL NOW!
TEAR OUT THEIR T'ROATS!
EHHH- -DEEE!
GO!
WE GOTTA GO! WE GOTTA GO, NOW!
DAMMIT!
SCHEPSEL, YOU STUPID BRUTE!
SSFFZZZZZZ
GLUGGG
PEDDLES, YOU'VE GOT TO BE KIDDING! IT'S GOTTA BE 600 MILES.
THE FASTER YOU START THE FASTER WE GET THERE.

THE *FASTER* WE LEAVE THIS HELLHOLE, THE *BETTER*.

KABOOM

AS I SIT HERE AND SCRIBBLE DOWN MY ADVENTURES, I CAN TELL YOU AT THAT MOMENT, IT STARTED TO FEEL LIKE A *FOOL'S ERRAND*.

I COULDA MADE A *NICE* LIVING PRIVATEERIN' OR RUNNIN' RUM 'TWEEN THE ISLANDS AND THE MAINLAND.

AT THAT MOMENT, *NONE* OF IT SEEMED WORTH IT.

TWO DAYS SIXTEEN HOURS AND 19 MINUTES IS FAR TOO LONG TO BE UNDERWATER PUSHING THIS UNHOLY CONTRAPTION.

BY MY CALCULATIONS, WE SHOULD BE *VERY* CLOSE.

JESUS EDDIE, WE SHOULD BE OFF THE COAST OF PORTUGAL BY NOW.

THE AIR, ALREADY SOUR WITH SWEAT, IS STARTIN' TO GO STALE.

WELL IF BY PORTUGAL YOU MEAN THE CAROLINAS THEN BOA VINDA A PORTUGAL!

I'VE GOT NO IDEA HOW MUCH LONGER I CAN LAST.

LISTEN, WE'VE COME A LONG WAY. AND I *THOUGHT* IT WAS TIME YOU SHARED YOUR PLAN.

OF COURSE THERE'S A *BLOODY* PLAN. I JUST *DON'T* KNOW WHAT IT IS YET.

HE WAS RIGHT. I THOUGHT I HAD A PLAN. IT WAS SIMPLE. FIND THE BASTARD AND STICK A KNIFE IN HIS GUT. MAYBE EVEN SPIT IN HIS GOB.

THERE *IS* A PLAN, RIGHT?

DID YOU HEAR SOMETHING?

BUT I'M LEARNING HARD THAT THE ROAD TO FAILURE IS PAVED ON THE SKULLS OF GOOD INTENTIONS.

IT'S ALL BEEN ON GIANT CLUSTER-CLUTCH.

AND SO THIS GIANT CLUSTER-CLUTCH JUST KEEPS BLOODY CLUTCHING AND CLUSTERING.
THIS ISN'T PART OF THE PLAN, IS IT?
HELLS BELLS. DON'T THE DEAD JUS' WANNA STAY DEAD?
AVAST THERE, HANNA TECH! STAND DOWN OR FACE THE WRATH OF GOD!
MY NAME WAS COLERIDGE. I AM CURSE-BOUND TO TELL YOU A STORY.

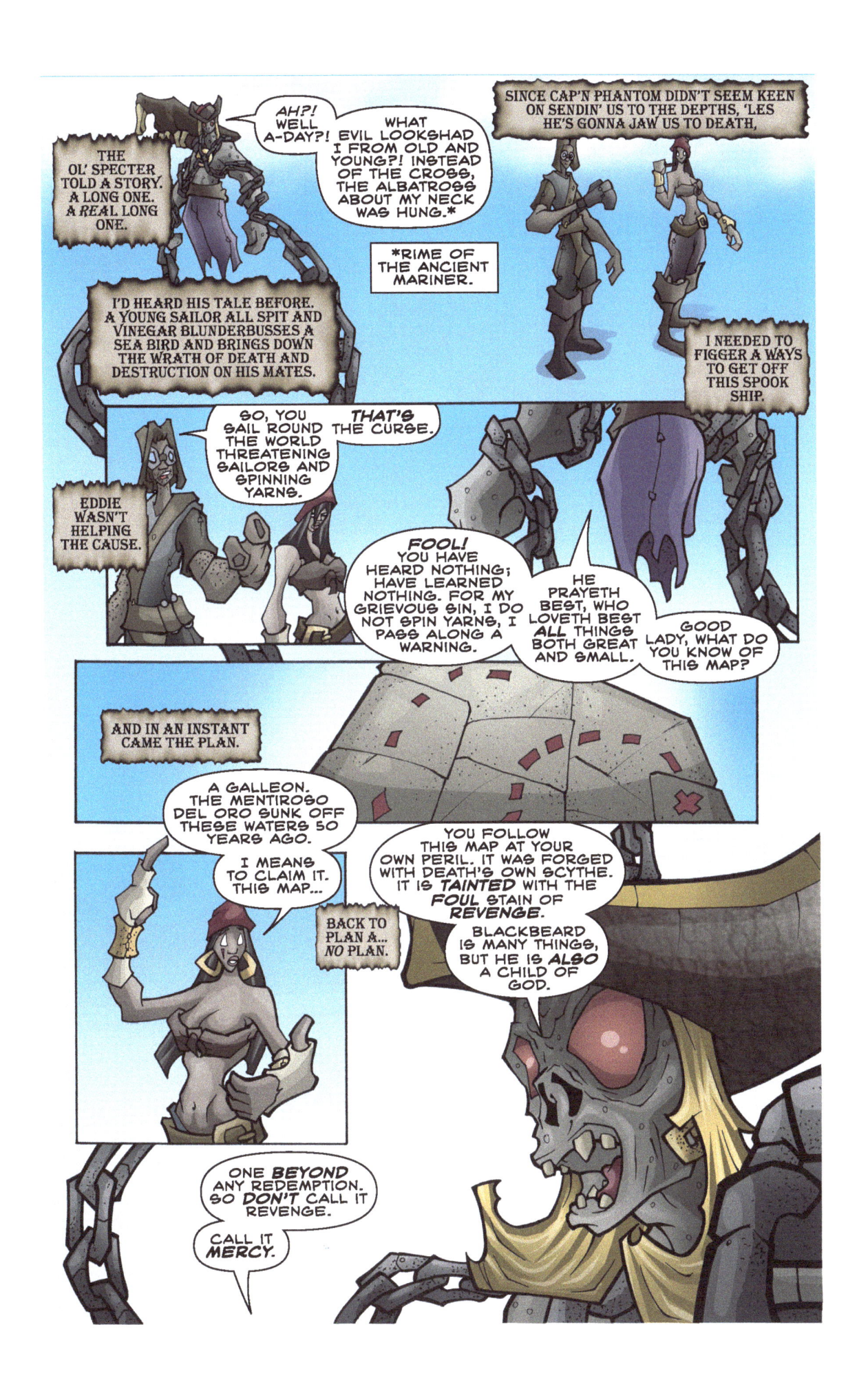

THE OL' SPECTER TOLD A STORY. A LONG ONE. A *REAL* LONG ONE.

AH?! WELL A-DAY?! WHAT EVIL LOOKSHAD I FROM OLD AND YOUNG?! INSTEAD OF THE CROSS, THE ALBATROSS ABOUT MY NECK WAS HUNG.*

SINCE CAP'N PHANTOM DIDN'T SEEM KEEN ON SENDIN' US TO THE DEPTHS, 'LES HE'S GONNA JAW US TO DEATH,

*RIME OF THE ANCIENT MARINER.

I'D HEARD HIS TALE BEFORE. A YOUNG SAILOR ALL SPIT AND VINEGAR BLUNDERBUSSES A SEA BIRD AND BRINGS DOWN THE WRATH OF DEATH AND DESTRUCTION ON HIS MATES.

I NEEDED TO FIGGER A WAYS TO GET OFF THIS SPOOK SHIP.

SO, YOU SAIL ROUND THE WORLD THREATENING SAILORS AND SPINNING YARNS.

THAT'S THE CURSE.

EDDIE WASN'T HELPING THE CAUSE.

FOOL! YOU HAVE HEARD NOTHING; HAVE LEARNED NOTHING. FOR MY GRIEVOUS SIN, I DO NOT SPIN YARNS, I PASS ALONG A WARNING.

HE PRAYETH BEST, WHO LOVETH BEST *ALL* THINGS BOTH GREAT AND SMALL.

GOOD LADY, WHAT DO YOU KNOW OF THIS MAP?

AND IN AN INSTANT CAME THE PLAN.

A GALLEON. THE MENTIROSO DEL ORO SUNK OFF THESE WATERS 50 YEARS AGO.

I MEANS TO CLAIM IT. THIS MAP...

YOU FOLLOW THIS MAP AT YOUR OWN PERIL. IT WAS FORGED WITH DEATH'S OWN SCYTHE. IT IS *TAINTED* WITH THE *FOUL* STAIN OF *REVENGE*.

BACK TO PLAN A... *NO PLAN.*

BLACKBEARD IS MANY THINGS, BUT HE IS *ALSO* A CHILD OF GOD.

ONE *BEYOND* ANY REDEMPTION. SO *DON'T* CALL IT REVENGE.

CALL IT *MERCY*.

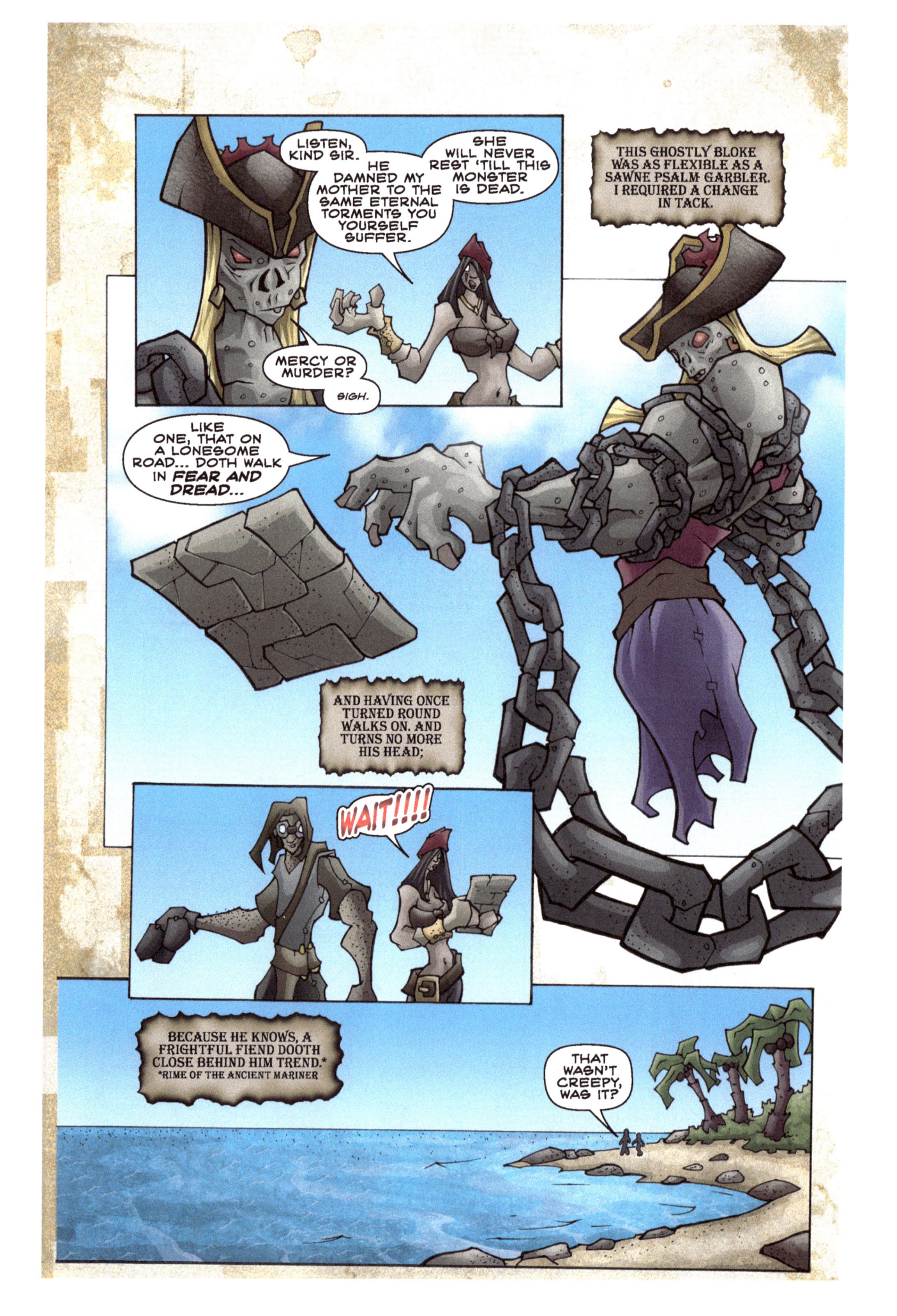

LISTEN, KIND SIR. HE DAMNED MY MOTHER TO THE SAME ETERNAL TORMENTS YOU YOURSELF SUFFER.

SHE WILL NEVER REST 'TILL THIS MONSTER IS DEAD.

THIS GHOSTLY BLOKE WAS AS FLEXIBLE AS A SAWNE PSALM GARBLER. I REQUIRED A CHANGE IN TACK.

MERCY OR MURDER?

SIGH.

LIKE ONE, THAT ON A LONESOME ROAD... DOTH WALK IN *FEAR AND DREAD*...

AND HAVING ONCE TURNED ROUND WALKS ON. AND TURNS NO MORE HIS HEAD;

WAIT!!!!

BECAUSE HE KNOWS, A FRIGHTFUL FIEND DOTH CLOSE BEHIND HIM TREAD.*
*RIME OF THE ANCIENT MARINER

THAT WASN'T CREEPY, WAS IT?

YOU'VE GOT GIZMOS THAT SHOOT FIRE, TRAVEL UNDER THE SEA, BUT YOU DIDN'T BRING ANYTHING TO CUT THROUGH THE BLOODY BRUSH?
WHAT KIND OF GENIUS ARE YOU?
THE DON'T-OWN-A-SWORD KIND.
SO CLOSE.
TELL ME YOU JUST DIDN'T...
IF YOU WERE A BLOODTHIRSTY BUCCANEER AND HIS WAS YOUR SECRET ISLAND, WHERE'S THE WELCOMING COMMITTEE?
SNAP!
WELL, WELL, WELL. WHACHOO S'POSE WE GOTS OURSELVES HERE?
BRING ME TO BLACKBEARD YOU CLOTTED CARCASS!
YOU'SE NOT IN A POSITION TO DEMANDS NUFFIN' DARLIN'.
I JUS' MIGHT WANNA PIECE OF YOUR FINE HIDE.

SO LOOK WHO'S NOW ALL GROWED UP AND LOOKIN' TO PUT A BULLET IN DADDY'S NEAC.
ALL PLANNED AND WHATNOT, BUT YOU FORGOT ONE TINY DETAIL.
ENLIGHTEN ME.
NEITHER OF YOU WHELPS GOT THE STONES TO PULL THE TRIGGER.
LASS, YOU AIN'T NOTHING MORE THAN A PIMPLE ON MY ARSE. I EVEN GIVE YOU THE TIME OF DAY CUZ I LIKED YOUR MA.
MISSY, THIS AIN'T NO GAME AND YOU AIN'T NO PIRATE.
YOU JUST PLAY DRESS UP IN A DASHER JACKET AND LOOK FOR BURIED TREASURE.
YOU WANT TO SEE WHAT PIRATING'S REALLY LIKE?
TRY ME, YOU BLOATED CODFISH!!

I SAW HER EYES, AND I KNEW I'D BEEN HOMSWOGGLED.

BUT THEM EYES ALSO GAVE WAY THAT SHE WAS NECK DEEP IN BILGE WATER.

WHAT? YOU DIDN'T KNOW SHE WASN'T REALLY BLIND? PLAYING YOU FOR A FOOL. I THOUGHT IT KINDA ADDED TO HER CHARM.

PICK A NUMBER... ONE OR TWO?

I DON'T UNDERSTAND.

IT'S SIMPLE, YOU WUZ ASKED TO CHOOSE, ONE... OR TWO.

UH, TWO.

I'M GLAD YA DIDN'T PICK ONE. I DIDN'T WANT TO WASTE A BULLET.

AND LIKE SHE WAS NO MORE THAN A CHICKEN BONE, THEY THREW HER OUT.

AAAAAIIIIEEEE

THE WAY I SEE IT, I SIMPLY REMOVED A THREAT. SO I ASK...
YOU JUST KEEP THINKING THAT LASS, I LIKE THAT.
ARE YOU THREATENING ME?
I LOOKED AND I LOOKED. TRYING TO FIND SOME SLIVER THAT THIS BRUTE WAS NOT ONLY BLOOD OF MY BLOOD, BUT HUMAN IN ANY WAY, SHAPE OR FORM.
YOU FIGGER IT OUT.
THEN I SAW SOMETHING I DIDN'T EXPECT TO FIND.
KIN OR NO, I'LL RIP YER HEART OUT FASTER THAN YOU CAN SAY JACK ROBINSON!
BEHIND ALL THE BRAVADO, BEHIND THE FAÇADE OF A CUTTHROAT BLAGGARD, THERE WAS NOTHING MORE THAN A OVERGROWN, BLUSTERING, SCHOOLYARD BULLY.
SO I DID WHAT ANY RIGHT-MINDED PAPER-SKULL WOULD DO. I TURNED AWAY.
INSOLENT LITTLE BITCH!!! I AM BLACKBEARD!
NO ONE TURNS THEIR BACK ON ME!

HE BLOODY SHOT ME IN MY BLOODY BACK! WHAT A RUTTLING COWERD!!
KKPLUGKG
GIVE MY REGARDS TO BEELZEBUB!

IT'S *COLD*. I FELT THE ICY FINGER OF THE *EVER AFTER* SCRATCHING MY SPINE.

THIS *AIN'T* OVER.

AIN'T YOU DEAD YET, MISSY? YOU MUST BE A TEACH. HARD TO KILL. BUT...

Skreeeeeeeee!

AN ORPHAN'S CURSE WOULD DRAG TO HELL A SPIRIT FROM ON HIGH; *BUT OH!* MORE HORRIBLE THAN THAT IS THE CURSE IN A DEAD MAN'S EYE!

OH MUDDER MARY FULLA GRAPES...WHAT'S THE BLOODYREST? WHAT MANNER OF BLACK MAGIC IS THIS?

GET TO THE QUEEN ANNE!

I'LL DEAL WITH THE PAIN. I JUST NEED ANOTHER CHANCE.

IT'S *OVER* FOR NOW...YOU'RE *HURT*.

I UNDERESTIMATED THE BASTARD. NOT AGAIN. WITH BLESSINS FROM ABOVE, I'LL HAVE HIM DANCIN' THE DUSTMAN'S JIG.

IT DOESN'T LOOK LIKE YOU'RE TOO FAR OFF.

THE VERY DEEP DID ROT, O' CHRIST! THAT EVER THIS SHOULD BE.
YEA **SLIMY** THINGS DID CRAWL WITH LEG UPON THE SLIMY SEA.
SIR, ALL THE DOORS ARE STUCK! THAT ALBATROSS...
THEN GET OFF YOUR ARSE A' RID ME OF THAT **BLASTED PIGEON!**
BLAM!
WE NEED A SHIP. WE CAN'T LET HIM GET TOO FAR AHEAD OF US.
I'M NOT SURE WE'RE GOING TO NEED ONE.

I'VE WITNESSED A NUMBER OF EVENTS THAT MIGHT DRIVE A SANER PERSON TO KEEP SHEEP BY MOONLIGHT. BUT I SWEAR ON MY FATHER'S LIFE THAT THE GREEN FOG SLOWLY ATE AWAY AT THE TOWER, THE CREW, EVERYTHING; LIKE A CORPSE TURNING TO DUST.

FFSSSZZZ

Panel 1
"THE DEAD IS RISIN'!"
"WE'RE THE DEAD, BUCCO."

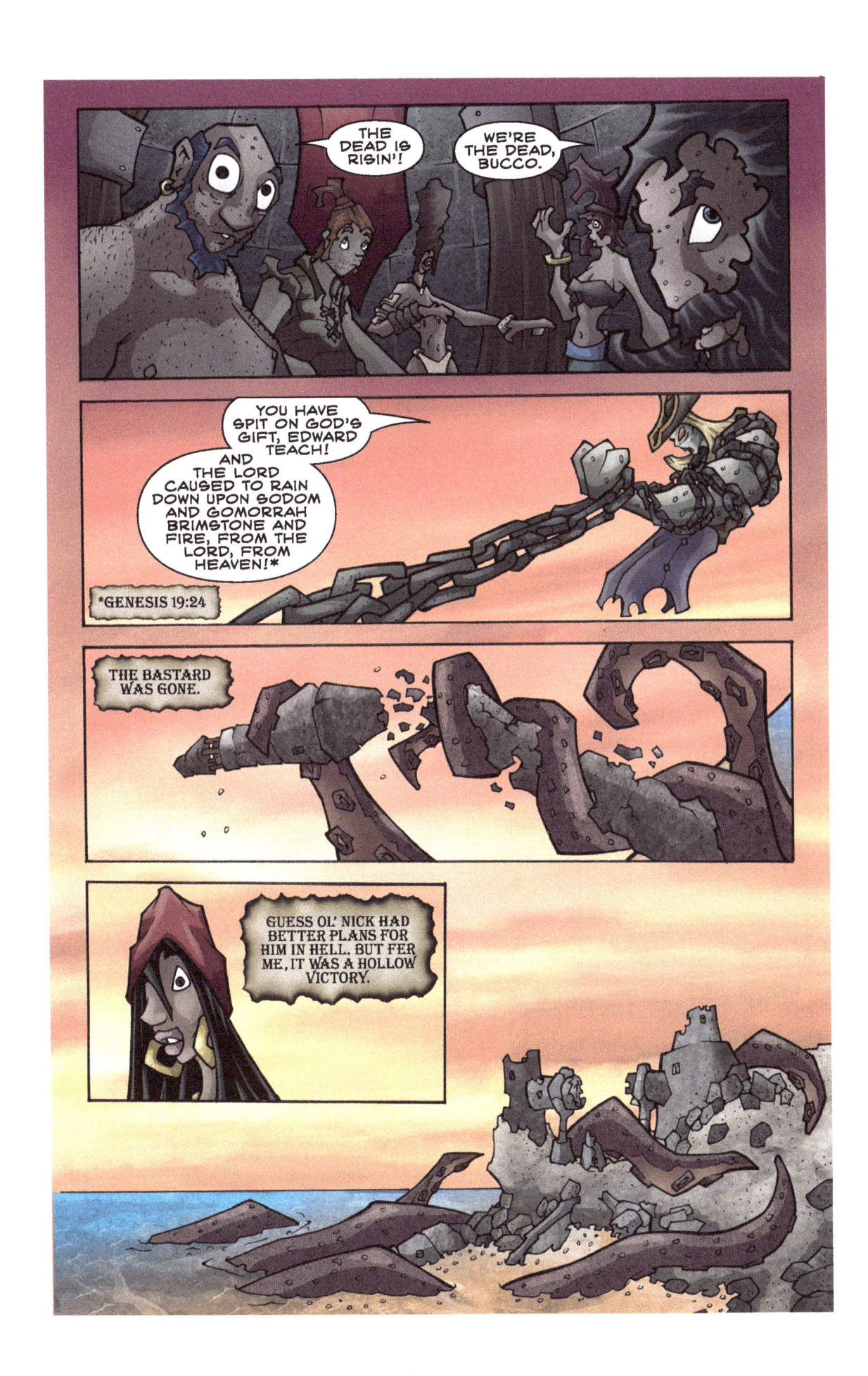

Panel 2
"YOU HAVE SPIT ON GOD'S GIFT, EDWARD TEACH! AND THE LORD CAUSED TO RAIN DOWN UPON SODOM AND GOMORRAH BRIMSTONE AND FIRE, FROM THE LORD, FROM HEAVEN!*"

*GENESIS 19:24

Panel 3
THE BASTARD WAS GONE.

Panel 4
GUESS OL' NICK HAD BETTER PLANS FOR HIM IN HELL. BUT FER ME, IT WAS A HOLLOW VICTORY.

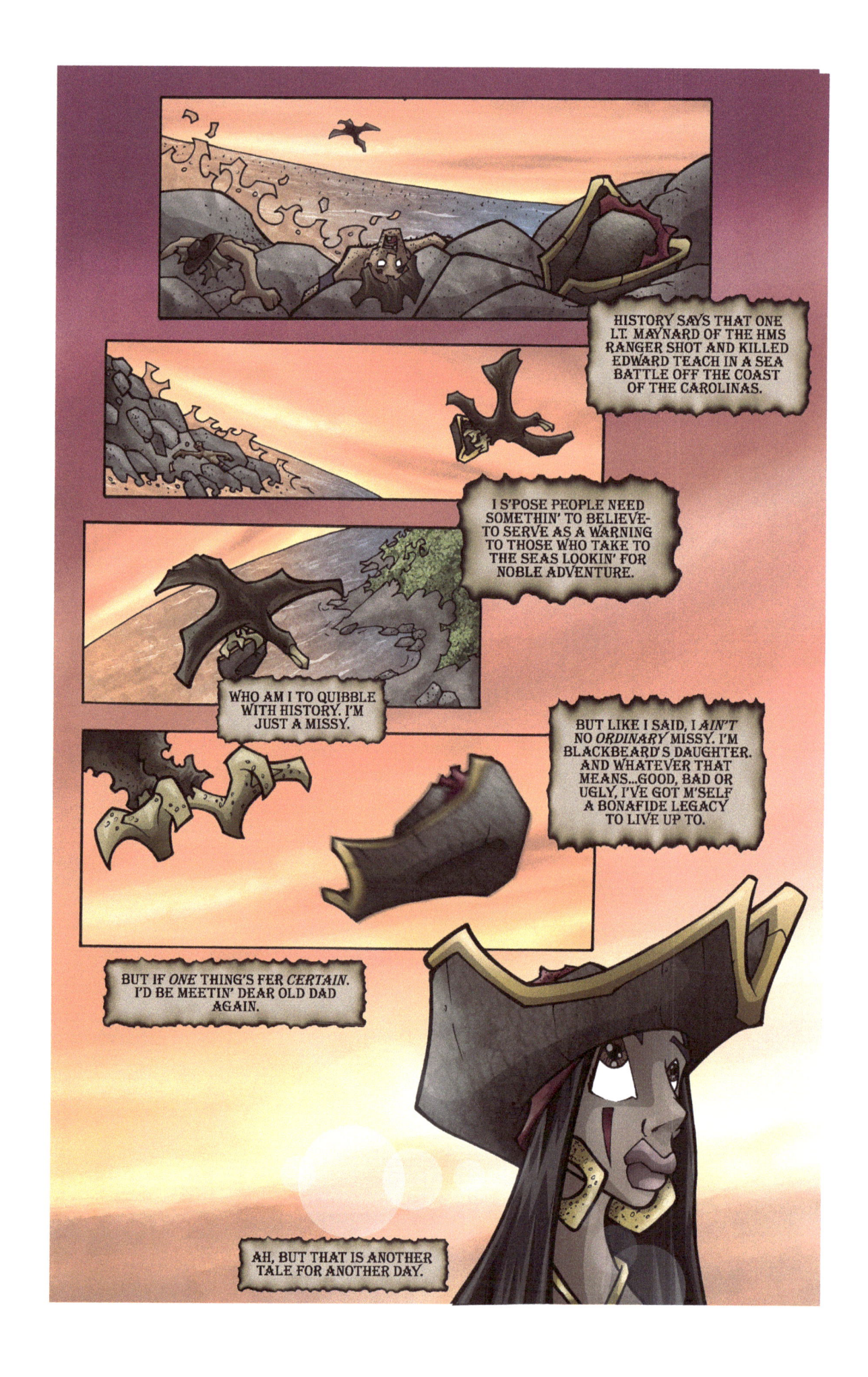

HISTORY SAYS THAT ONE LT. MAYNARD OF THE HMS RANGER SHOT AND KILLED EDWARD TEACH IN A SEA BATTLE OFF THE COAST OF THE CAROLINAS.

I S'POSE PEOPLE NEED SOMETHIN' TO BELIEVE- TO SERVE AS A WARNING TO THOSE WHO TAKE TO THE SEAS LOOKIN' FOR NOBLE ADVENTURE.

WHO AM I TO QUIBBLE WITH HISTORY. I'M JUST A MISSY.

BUT LIKE I SAID, I *AIN'T* NO *ORDINARY* MISSY. I'M BLACKBEARD'S DAUGHTER. AND WHATEVER THAT MEANS...GOOD, BAD OR UGLY, I'VE GOT M'SELF A BONAFIDE LEGACY TO LIVE UP TO.

BUT IF *ONE* THING'S FER *CERTAIN*. I'D BE MEETIN' DEAR OLD DAD AGAIN.

AH, BUT THAT IS ANOTHER TALE FOR ANOTHER DAY.

Chapter 5

Blackbeard's daughter, *Hanna*, out of the shadow of her father, stands in challenge of a storm...

No storm at sea is the same, and I've seen my share. But this one shakes even me.

I can't let the crew know, though...they're already shaking...but still, there's something very strange about this storm. I can't resist its pull on me.

Danger has always been intoxicating, I guess.

GOING ANY FARTHER MIGHT CRACK THE BOAT IN TWAIN, CAP'N...
"...THE CREW'S NERVES ARE SPIKED-- TEMPERS ARE READY TO ERUPT.
"AND THOSE WATERS AREN'T HELPING THE MOOD ANY."
"WE'LL WAIT A BIT--GIVE IT TIME TO SETTLE. BUT WE'RE NOT CHANGIN' COURSE, MAGNA.
"THOSE WATERS MIGHT SCARE YOU YELLOW-BELLIED BUNCH..."
...BUT I'VE SEEN WORSE.

Captain Purloin beat any storm I ever had to go through. Lyin' my way into his good graces, promising him we could split the treasure when we found it...
LET'S MAKE A DEAL, PURLOIN.
WHAT'D YOU HAVE IN MIND?
HEH HEH...
Hanna!

...givin' myself to him, his rotten, stinking hands all over me, in his bed.

Gaining just enough trust to take what I needed from him. It was the easiest thing in the world after that. Once he was drugged and shut his eyes, I had his half of the loot out the door before he let out his first snore...

ZZZZZZZZZ

...and he's been after me ever since. Now there's a storm to be weary of.

Still, Captain Purloin is just a man, and like all men, he's led by lust...

...lust and superstition. They can be easily distracted.

I have the bravest crew on the sea, and they're all women. I haven't the time for men.

They're too easily beaten...

COME ON, LADIES!

PULL!

ARGH!

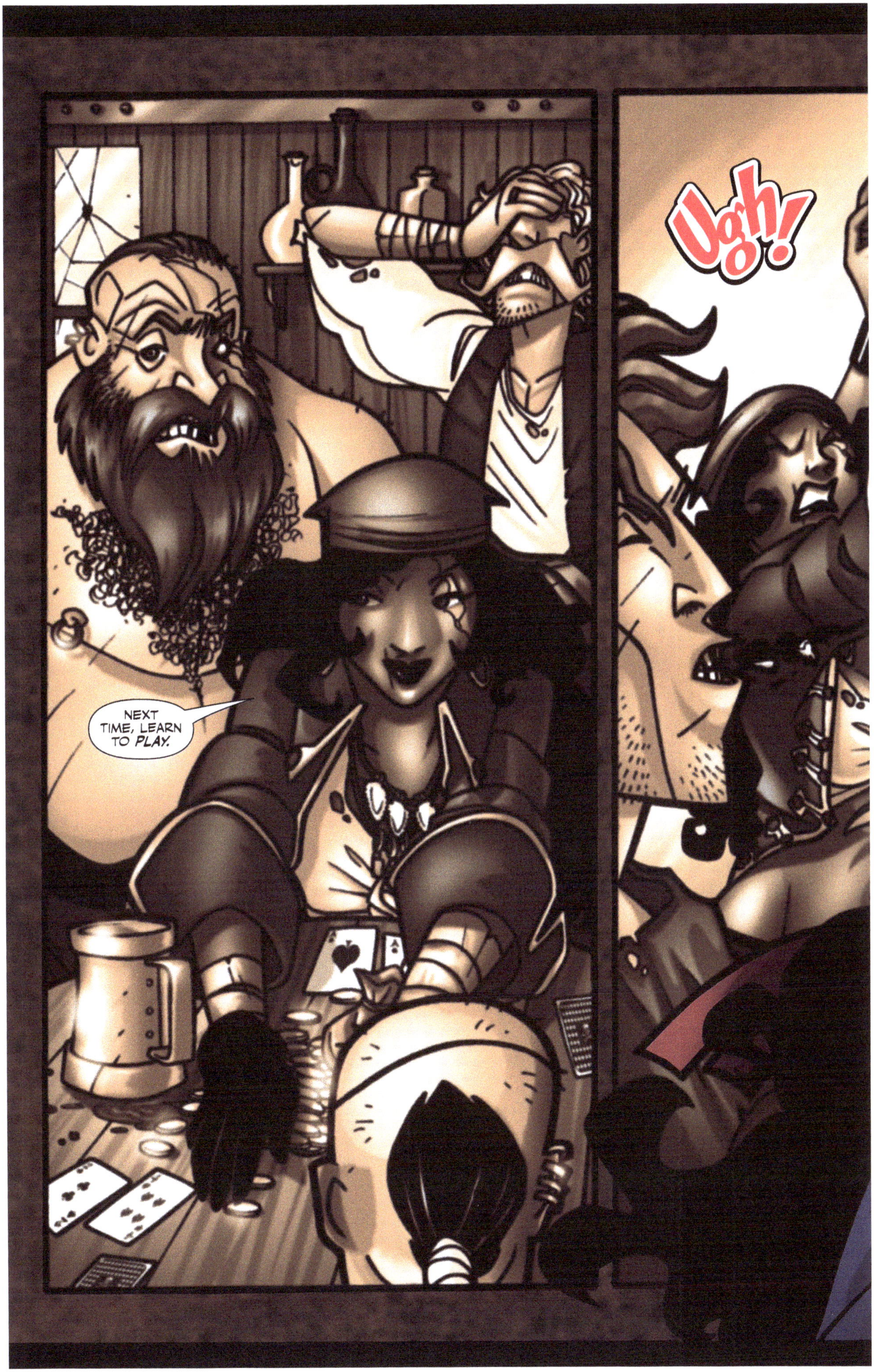
Ugh!
NEXT TIME, LEARN TO PLAY.

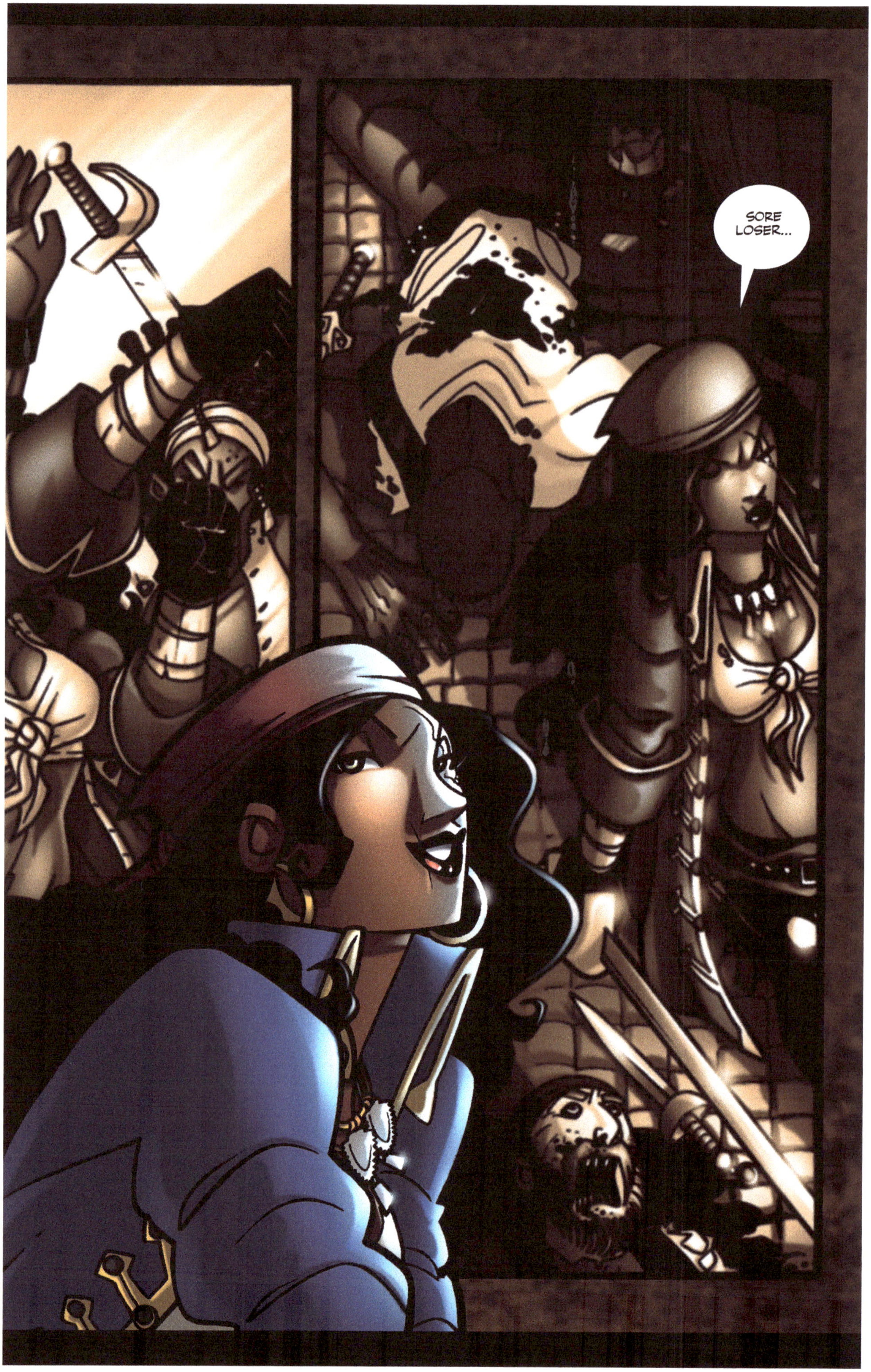
SORE LOSER...

The storm has subsided, and Hanna's ship slowly edges into the still turbulent waters, now littered with wreckage and debris from an unfortunate ship's *last* voyage.

Among the wreckage are the lifeless bodies of a once vibrant crew.

THAT COULDA BEEN US!

NAH.

THE CAP'N WOULDNA LET THAT *HAPPEN.*

It's always deadly quiet after a storm such as this. Too quiet.

The unseen can break the mind just as fast as a storm breaks the bones.

"KEEP YOUR *WITS*, MATES.

"I WON'T HAVE ANY YELLOW BELLIES ON *MY* SHIP."

"WHAT'S THIS?"

The wreckage and bloated bodies are a macabre trail leading Hanna's attention to a small island.

There looks to me to be bounty aplenty on the shore. Purloin's ship isn't that fast, and his crew is feeble. We have time, methinks.

"HEAD FOR THAT PIECE OF ROCK. WE'RE GOING TO MAKE A QUICK STOP. SEE WHAT WE CAN FIND. SEE WHAT'S LEFT BEHIND."

"AYE, CAP'N!"

WHAT USE IS THIS?
WHAT COULD HAVE SURVIVED *THAT* STORM?
BY WHAT *I'M* SEEING, NOT MUCH.
THERE'S SO LITTLE WHAT *MADE* IT...
WHY EVEN *BOTHER?*
WE TAKE WHAT WE CAN WHEN WE CAN *GET* IT, LADIES...

They're discontent. I can tell. Probably think I'm crazy for taking to land with Purloin hot on our heels.

But then, crazy is good for a pirate. Crazy and feared go hand and hand.

From behind the cover of shade and rock, someone *watches* with great interest. Someone who has waited for just such an occasion. Someone who desperately needs to get his hands on a *ship*.

He studies the captain and the crew. They're strong. But not stronger than desperate *will power*.

Steal the ship and leave the crew on the island. *There's a plan!*

LOAD EVERYTHING ON BOARD. WE'LL DIVIDE IT LATER.

BEGGIN' YOUR PARDON, CAP'N--BUT THERE AIN'T MUCH TO *DIVIDE.*

One fierce look from Hanna *quiets* the groans of discontent.

hanna's glare is not directed at Magna's comment, though. A quick movement has caught her attention. Something *lurking* at the mouth of a cave.

What little bounty this be, it's mine. I'll not share it with any shadow *skulker.*

hanna motions for a few of her mates to follow her...

Into the mouth of the cave they go.

Quiet. *Stealth*...

HANDS ON YOUR *HILTS*, MATES.

The darkness of the cave surrounds the crew, impeding their sight.

They are *unaware* of the figure pressed flat against the wall, *waiting* for them.

But Hanna's forewarning sense of danger has *never* let her down.

STUPID OF ME TO THINK THAT CAPTAIN WOULDN'T SEE ME-- WOULDN'T SEARCH ME OUT. AND SHE DOESN'T LOOK THE TYPE TO GIVE UP EASILY.
SEARCH EVERY INCH OF THIS HOLE.
AS FAR BACK AS IT GOES AND AS DEEP AS HADES IF NEED BE.
I DON'T WANT SOMEONE ALIVE LAYING CLAIM TO WHAT'S OURS.

Suddenly, a figure *jumps out* from behind the cave wall, knocking Magna to the ground!

Oomph!

The crew *rushes* in to subdue him!

GET HIM!

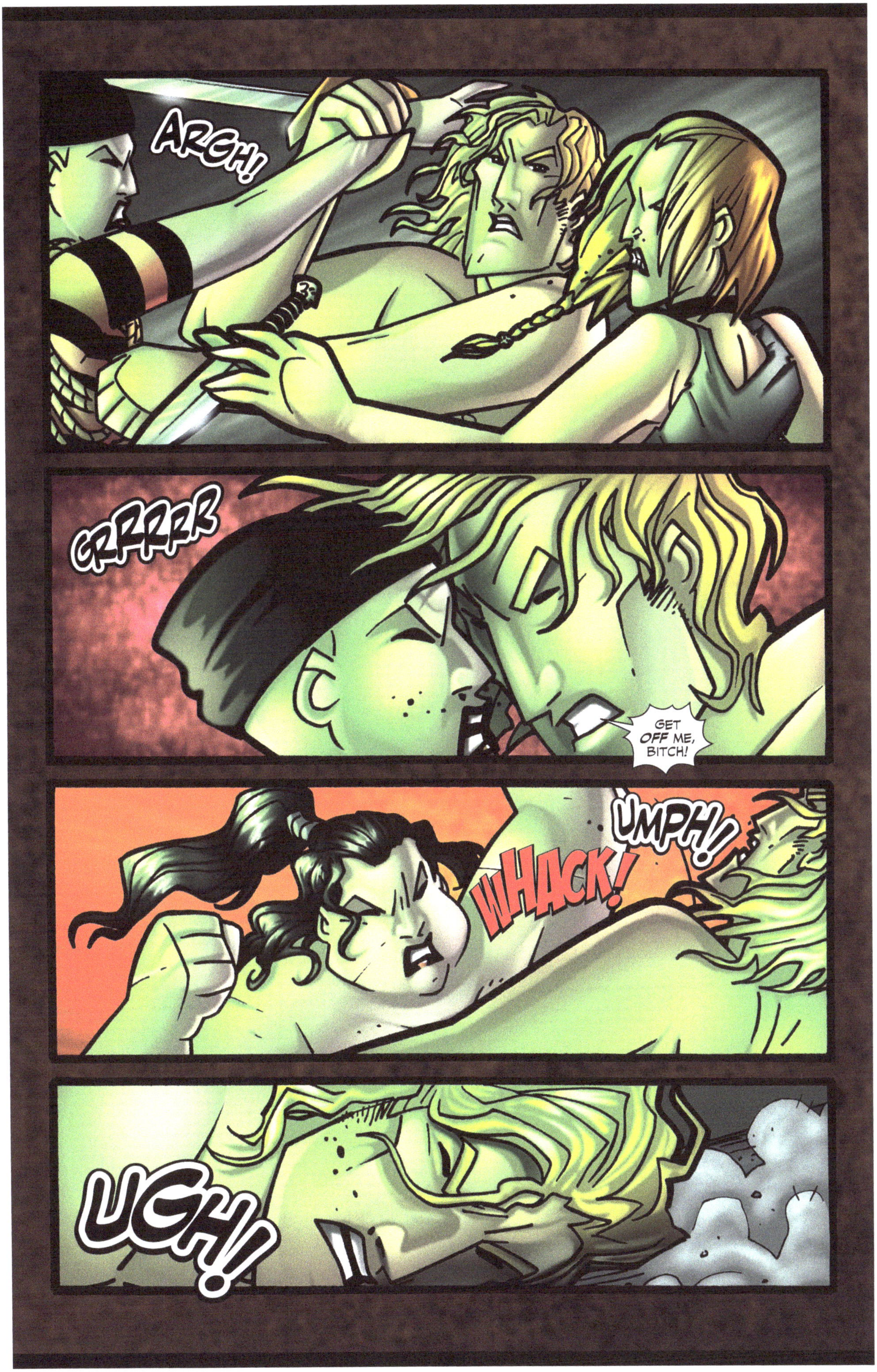
ARGH!
GRRRRR
GET OFF ME, BITCH!
UMPH!
WHACK!
UGH!

Defeated now by the mighty blow of the pirate's swing, the mysterious cave-lurker finds himself at the tip of *Hanna's* sword!

WHAT HAPPE...

DON'T *MOVE*, BLOKE.

ENJOY THE LAST FEW BREATHS YOU *HAVE*.

As the crew's eyes adapt to the sparse light of the cave, they see a handsome young man lying on the ground. He stares at Hanna defiantly.
WHAT A DISH...
YES, MA'AM.
DEAD MEAT!

Chapter 6

Captain Hanna and her crew have make land off the shores of a small island, the surrounding waters and beach strewn with the wreckage from some unfortunate vessel's fate. While picking through the miniscule bounty to be had, Captain Hanna has discovered they are *not alone* on the island...

"DON'T WORRY YOUR *PRETTY* HEAD."

"I'LL MAKE THIS AS QUICK AND PAINLESS AS POSSIBLE."

FINISH COLLECTING WHAT YOU CAN. I'LL DEAL WITH THIS SWINE.
IF YOU DON'T, I WILL, CAP'N.
LAST WORDS, PRETTY BOY?
HOW DO YOU GET YOURSELF OUTTA THIS ONE, ROBBIE BUCKLE?

WAIT! I CAN BE VERY *HELPFUL* TO YOU, CAPTAIN!

YOUR CHARMS WON'T WORK ON *ME*.

I'VE GOT NO NEED FOR MEN.

NO. WHAT I MEAN IS--I CAN LEAD YOU TO A MUCH *GREATER* BOUNTY THAN THE PITTANCE WHAT WASHED UP ON THIS ISLAND.

BEYOND YOUR *WILDEST* DREAMS, MA'AM.

I'M LISTENING.
BUT, BE QUICK...
...LEST I LOSE MY PATIENCE.
AND YOU LOSE YOUR HEAD.

SACRIFICE THE GOLD. YOU'VE A MORE IMPORTANT TREASURE WAITING.
I KNOW OF AN ISLAND-- AN ISLAND ONLY I KNOW THE WAY TO.
THERE'S A STASH THERE--A GREAT HEAP OF TREASURE. MORE GOLD AND JEWELS THAN YOU COULD EVER DREAM OF-- PILED TO THE HEIGHTS OF THE CAVE IT LIES IN AND LINING ITS WALLS.
IT'S A SIGHT TO SEE, MA'AM.
WHY TELL ME OF THIS IF IT'S SO GREAT A TREASURE?
I NEED HELP TO GET IT.
I HAVE NO SHIP--I'LL SPLIT IT WITH YOU.

After a moment's hesitation, Hanna consents to his plea...
ALL RIGHT, THEN. I ACCEPT YOUR OFFER.
IT WAS VERY WISE OF YOU TO OFFER YOUR KNOWLEDGE OF SUCH A PLACE...
...and I'll take more than half, pretty one.
THERE WAS A SWORD TO MY NECK. I'M NO FOOL.
THE NAME'S ROBBIE BUCKLE...
WATCH YOURSELF!
IF I SO MUCH AS THINK YOU'RE DOUBLE-CROSSING ME, YOU'RE DEAD!
GOT IT?
gulp S-S-SURE.

the uncomfortable understanding is soon interrupted by a ruckus from outside the cave.

WHAT'S *THIS*?

IT'S NOT A *WHO*, MA'AM. **THE DEAD ARE RISING!**

THE DEAD NEED TO KNOW THEIR *PLACE*-- THAT BE UNDER MY *HEEL*!

I DON'T NEED ANY *MORE* OBSTACLES OF FLESH AND BONE!

The crew cut down zombies like hay in the field. But as one is slain another rises from the sand to take its place. They come after the ladies, one thing on their mind: *fresh meat!*
SQUISH
URGH!
GUUURRLY...
ARGH!
UGH! WHY ARE THE UGLY ONES ALWAYS ATTRACTED TO *ME?* HANDS OFF!

YOU'RE NOT MY TYPE-- TRUST ME!
MEN! ALWAYS LOSING THEIR HEADS OVER ME.
BANG
GIRL BRAINS...

I GUESS IF I WANT TO LEAVE THIS ROCK, I BETTER FOLLOW SUIT.
HOLD 'EM OFF, MATES! HACK THEIR ROTTEN HEADS OFF!
GRRRR!
BANG
GUUROGH!
HOW 'BOUT THIS, UGLY!
SPLAT
HUH...

THANKS...
NO PROBLEM... CAPTAIN.
WE'RE OUTNUMBERED! TO THE SHIP!
GET YOUR DEAD HANDS OFF MY FIRST MATE!
SWISH
GAAAAwwwww...
THE SEA TAKE ME! I ALMOST BECAME ZOMBIE FOOD.

I THOUGHT HE WAS DEAD. WHY'S HE STILL HANGING ABOUT?
I'VE GOT MY REASONS. THAT'S ALL YOU NEED KNOW.
I DUNNO-- I THINK IT'S A GOOD IDEA TO HAVE A PRETTY YOUNG THING ABOARD.
UMMMM...

>sigh<

THIS IS GONNA BE TOO EASY.

This is exactly why I don't run with men. Pretty diversions is all they are. I hope this is *worth* it.

HE SURE IS TASTY LOOKIN', CAP'N.

DON'T BECOME TOO USED TO HIM, LADIES. HE'S NOT WITH US *LONG*.

THAT'S TOO BAD...

BUT HE'S SO PURTY!

GOOD RIDDANCE!

Meanwhile, across the wide sea, chasing Hanna and her crew, **Captain Purloin's** hulking vessel ploughs through the waters unchallenged.

The captain is a determined man, despite his crew's quiet discord.

Though he knows the captain a hard man, the first mate, *Nicolas*, foolishly speaks his mind.

"'TIS *FOLLY* TO RUSH INTO ROUGH SEA, SIR."

"*SILENCE!* I WILL NOT BE QUESTIONED BY WHIMPERING *COWARDS*."

"ALL THIS FOR A *WOMAN*-- FOR THE PLEASURES HE CAN EASILY FIND AT *DOCK*."

"GRRRRR..."

UUUHHHHH
FILTHY SWINE!
gasp
ANYONE ELSE WANT TO SAY ANYTHING?
NO?
I THOUGHT NOT.

Back on Hanna's ship, the crew was warming up to their new, if *temporary,* member...
HEY, SWEET CHEEKS...WANNA PLAY SOMETIME?
I'LL PUT A STOP TO THIS!
QUIT YOUR CAROUSING AND GET BACK TO WORK! HIS JOB IS NOT TO *ENTERTAIN.*
AYE, CAP'N.
BUT WHAT *USE* IS HE IF NOT FOR LOOKS AND DALLIANCE? WE HAVE CREW *ENOUGH.*

AND YOU—MAKE CERTAIN YOU KNOW WHAT YOU'RE HERE FOR.

REMEMBER—NO CAVORTING WITH MY CREW.

THAT'S YOUR WARNING.

THAT'S FINE BY ME, CAPTAIN.

BELIEVE ME—I DON'T NEED THE DISTRACTION.

I'LL GET WHAT I'M AFTER EVEN IF EVERY VESSEL THAT SAILS ON THE SEA ENDS UP BENEATH IT.

ATTACHMENTS ARE A NUISANCE.

Suddenly the sky above them cracks; lightning flashes, burning the horizon. The ship is tossed like a feather on the wind.

HOLD FAST, LADIES! WE'RE IN FOR A ROUGH SPELL!

KEEP YOUR WITS!

YOUR WITS CAN'T SAVE YOU FROM THE SOURCE OF THIS STORM, CAPTAIN.

THIS WEATHER BE STRANGE, EVEN FOR THE SEA!
IT'S AS IF SOMETHING BRINGS THE *WRATH* OF THE SEA! A HARBINGER OF DEATH OR SOME UNLUCKY TOKEN!
UGH!
I HAVE AN IDEA WHAT IT MIGHT BE.

Panel 1: THAT LOOK ON YOUR FACE BESPEAKS OF FEAR AND KNOWING, ROBBIE BUCKLE.

Panel 2: "FOUL WEATHER SEEMS TO *FOLLOW* YOU."

Panel 3: 'TIS THE *WEATHER*, IS ALL. THE HIGH SEAS ARE PRECARIOUS...

YOU'RE A *LIAR!* AND I'M WEARY OF IT!

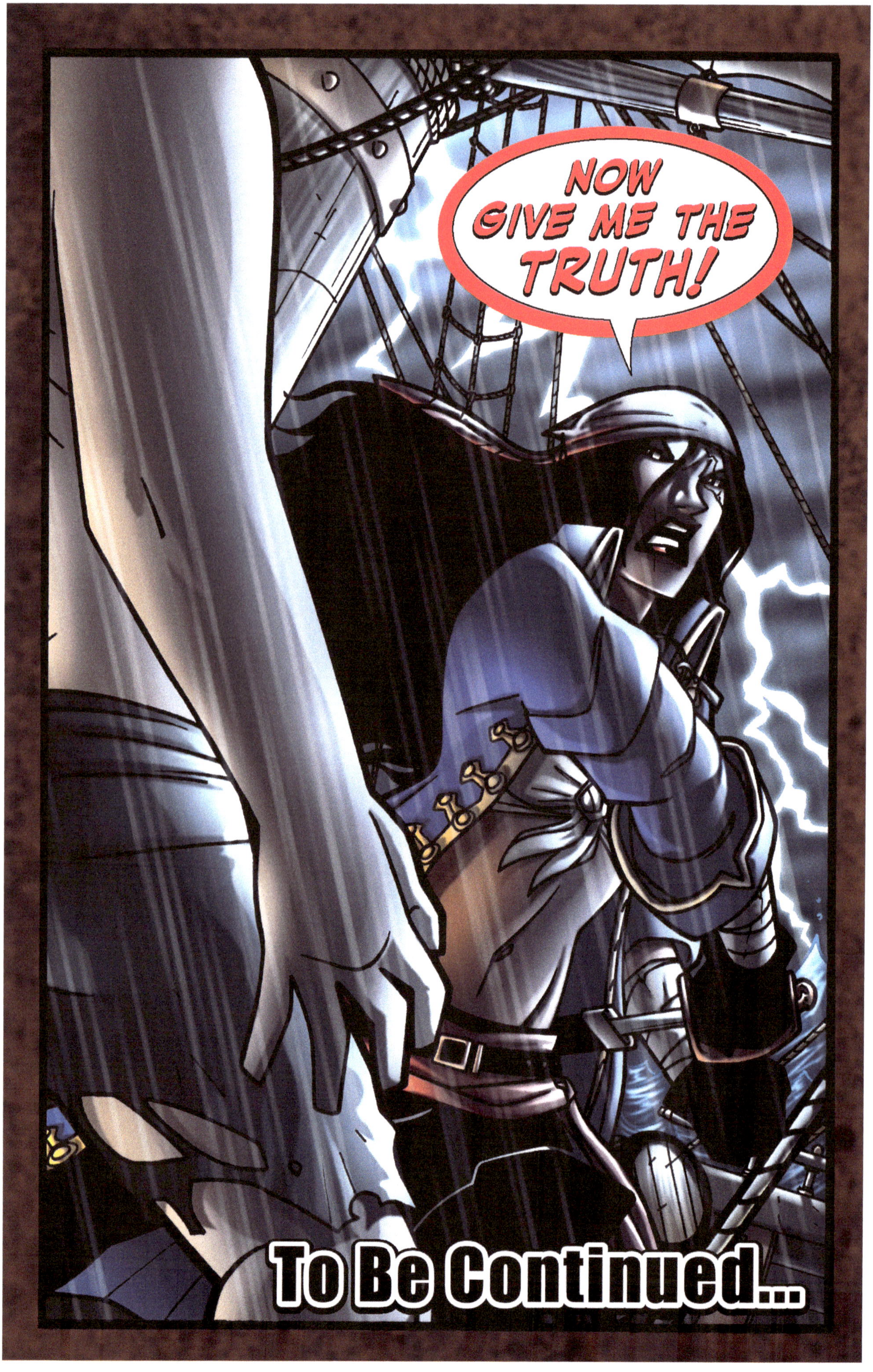
NOW GIVE ME THE TRUTH!
To Be Continued...

Chapter 7

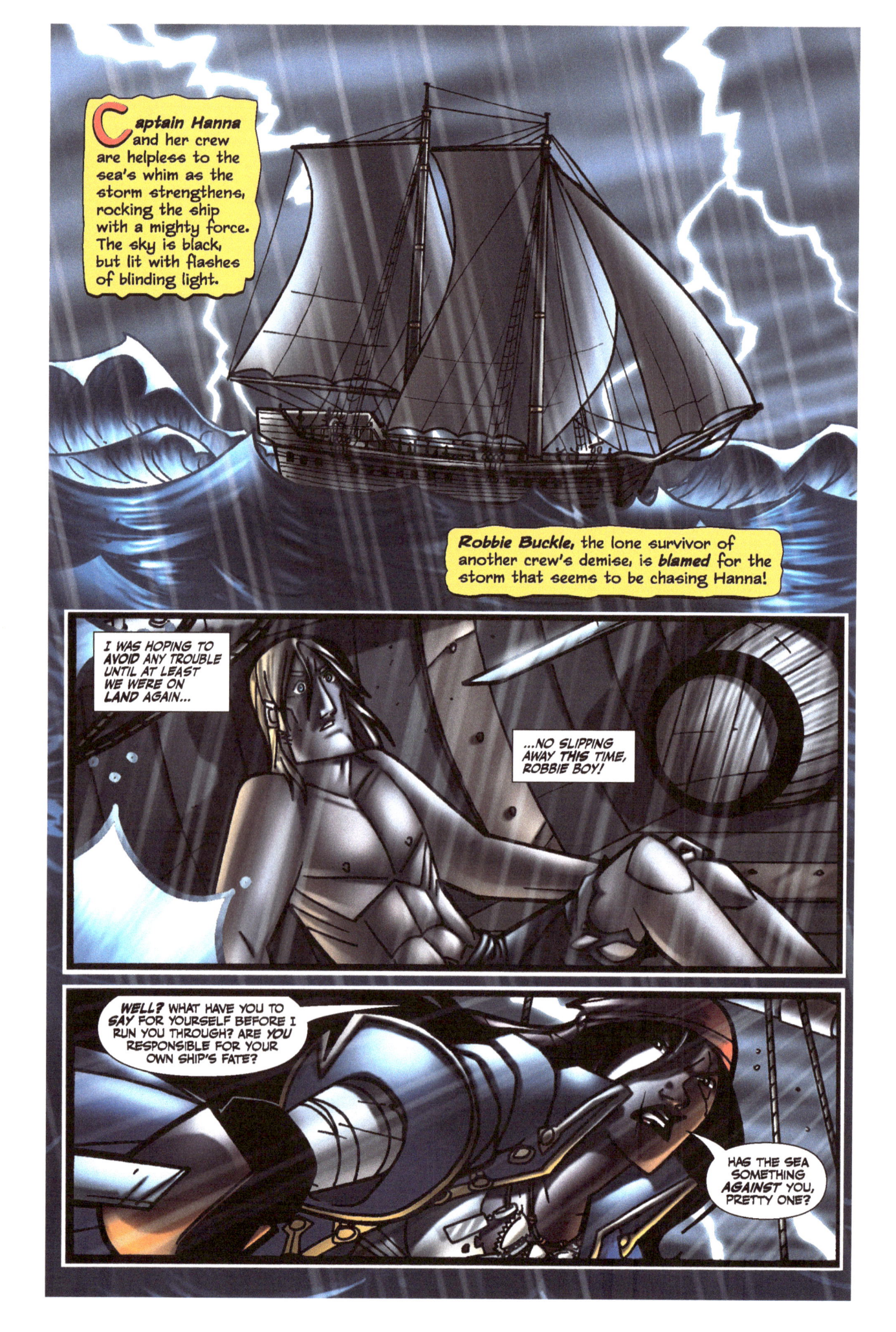

Captain Hanna and her crew are helpless to the sea's whim as the storm strengthens, rocking the ship with a mighty force. The sky is black, but lit with flashes of blinding light.

Robbie Buckle, the lone survivor of another crew's demise, is blamed for the storm that seems to be chasing Hanna!

I WAS HOPING TO AVOID ANY TROUBLE UNTIL AT LEAST WE WERE ON LAND AGAIN...

...NO SLIPPING AWAY THIS TIME, ROBBIE BOY!

WELL? WHAT HAVE YOU TO SAY FOR YOURSELF BEFORE I RUN YOU THROUGH? ARE YOU RESPONSIBLE FOR YOUR OWN SHIP'S FATE?

HAS THE SEA SOMETHING AGAINST YOU, PRETTY ONE?

"THE SHIP WAS NOT *MINE*, CAPTAIN.

"I WAS A HIDDEN GUEST-- A *STOWAWAY*. I NEEDED PASSAGE.

"THEY DIDN'T REALIZE I WAS WITH THEM UNTIL THE STORM WAS BEARING DOWN UPON US WITH ALL ITS FORCE. BY THEN IT WAS TOO *LATE*."

BEST TO LEAVE *OUT* THE PART WHERE THE ILL WEATHER WAS BLAMED ON *ME*. THEY WOULD HAVE THROWN ME OVERBOARD TOO IF I HADN'T PROMISED THEM A GREAT TREASURE--

--THE VERY ONE I'VE PROMISED TO CAPTAIN *HANNA*.

WHO KNOWS? MAYBE SHE'LL EVEN LIVE LONG ENOUGH TO SEE IT.

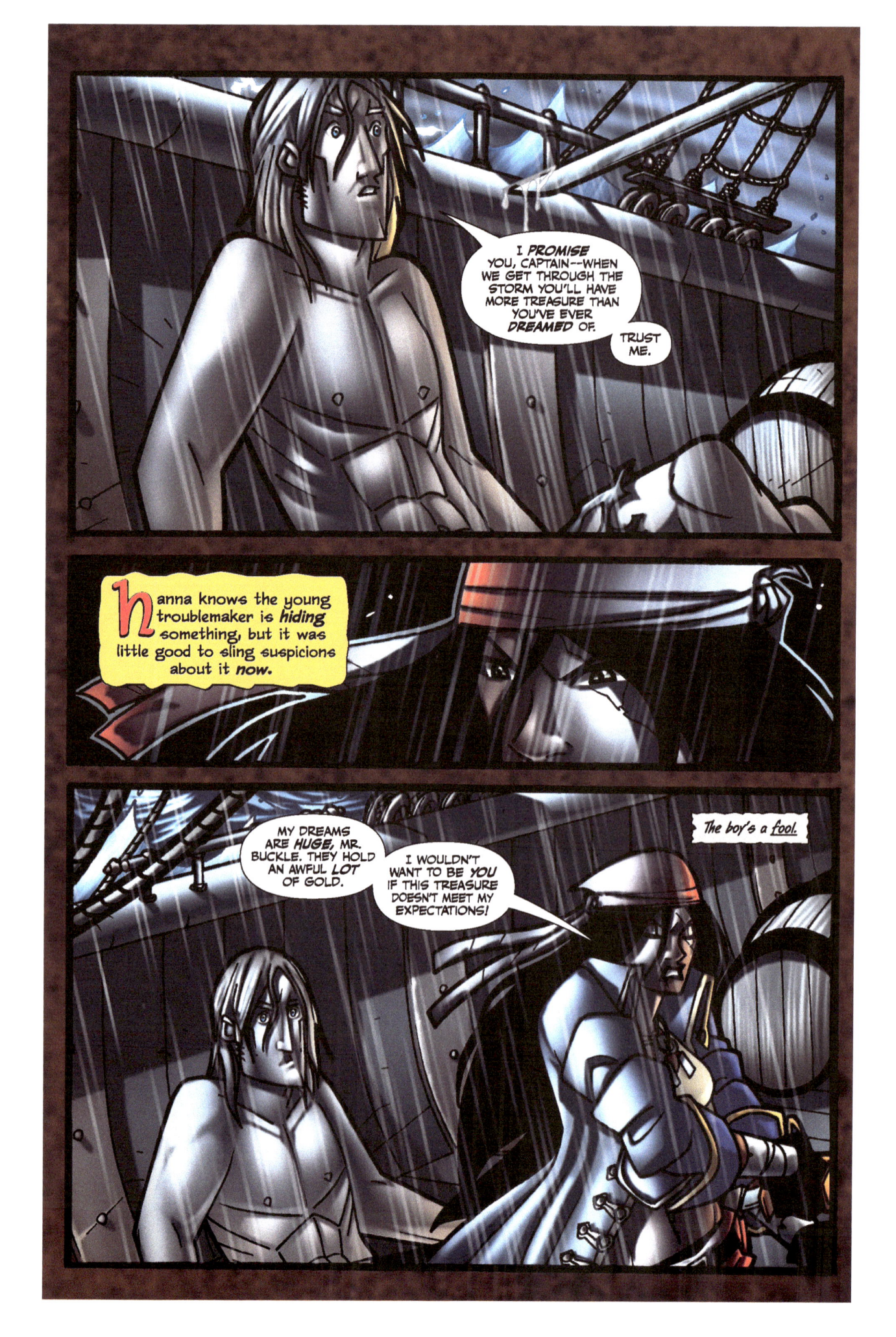

"I PROMISE YOU, CAPTAIN--WHEN WE GET THROUGH THE STORM YOU'LL HAVE MORE TREASURE THAN YOU'VE EVER DREAMED OF."

"TRUST ME."

hanna knows the young troublemaker is *hiding* something, but it was little good to sling suspicions about it *now*.

"MY DREAMS ARE *HUGE*, MR. BUCKLE. THEY HOLD AN AWFUL *LOT* OF GOLD."

"I WOULDN'T WANT TO BE *YOU* IF THIS TREASURE DOESN'T MEET MY EXPECTATIONS!"

The boy's a *fool.*

Suddenly, alarm is raised...

CAP'N! WE GOT *TROUBLE!*

SOMETHING'S HEADED *STRAIGHT* FOR US, AND IT'S *NOT* A PRETTY SIGHT!

NOT PRETTY AT ALL, CAP'N!

Rising from the water, a *massive wave* climbs and climbs to a terrifying height! Within its ripples and foam an angered intelligence *stares out* at the crew!

The roar of the wave is deafening...

...it only *strengthens* as it approaches!

Through the roar can be heard the war cry of a *sea god!* The great waves reach like hands for the ship...

Captain Hanna is *awestruck* for the first time in her life as she witnesses the sentient nature of the sea!

WHAT *IS* THIS?!
IF YOU'VE GOT A GOD, I'D CALL FOR HIS *HELP* NOW, MATES!
gasp
CAP'N, ARE YOU *SEEING* WHAT WE'RE *SEEING?*
Dammit! What's this boy brought to us?
I'M SEEING A WATERY *VENGEANCE,* MATES!
HOLD ON TO YOUR *BREECHES!*
HE'S *COME* FOR ME AT LAST...

A great roar of thunder and lightning breaks in on the crew's thoughts! A surge from the sea creates chaos on deck! And from the guts of the ocean comes but a single name:
ROBBIE BUCKLE!

The crew is *scattered* over the deck, *unbalanced* and *blinded* by the water!

AAAAGH!

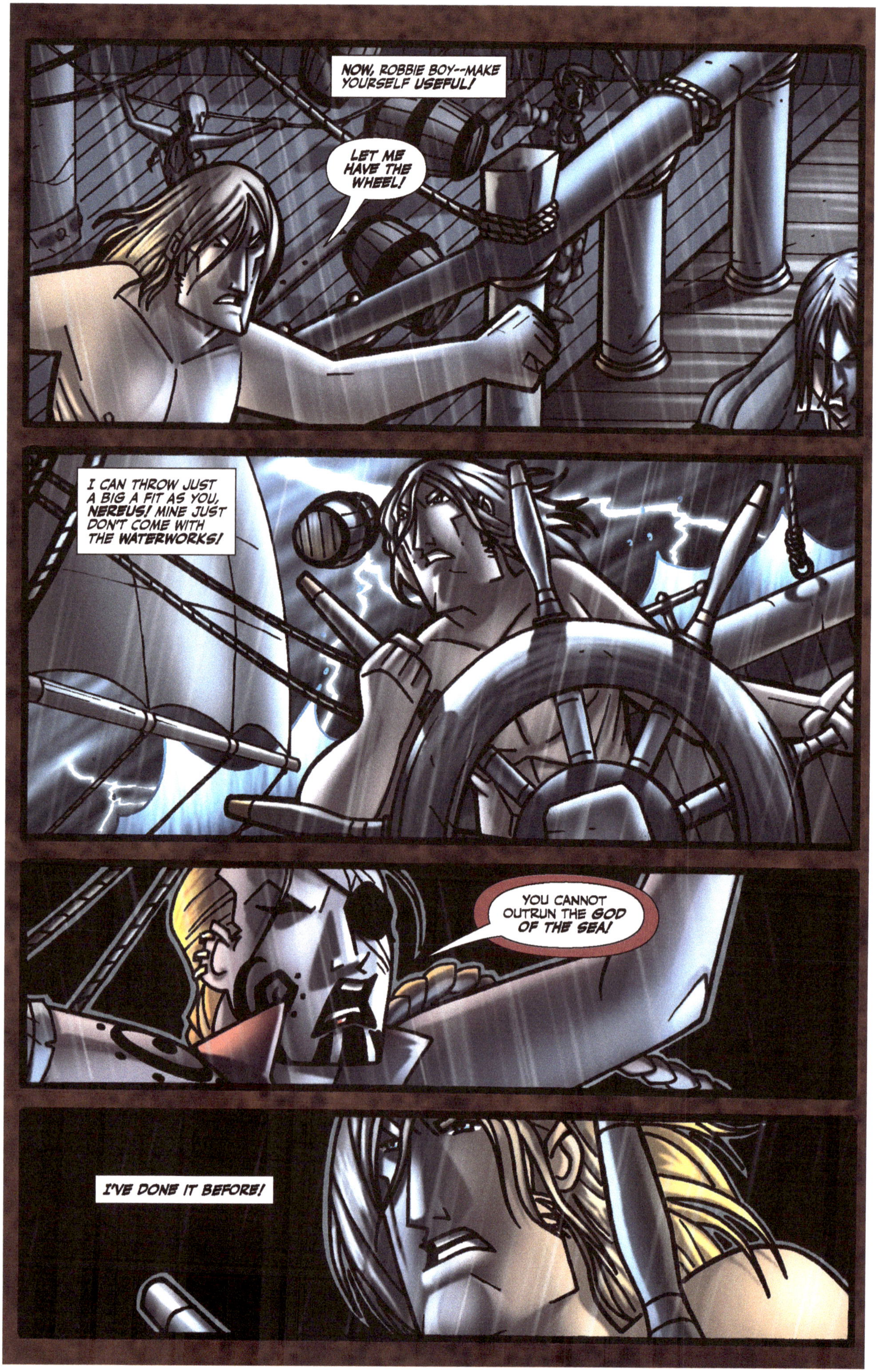
NOW, ROBBIE BOY--MAKE YOURSELF USEFUL!
LET ME HAVE THE WHEEL!
I CAN THROW JUST A BIG A FIT AS YOU, NEREUS! MINE JUST DON'T COME WITH THE WATERWORKS!
YOU CANNOT OUTRUN THE GOD OF THE SEA!
I'VE DONE IT BEFORE!

I might as well help the fool! I hope he knows what he's doing!

The sea god **Nereus** towers over the ship, his moans shaking the corners of the world!

ROBBIE BUCKLE!

THIS IS *IT*, LADIES! WE'RE *SEA URCHIN* FROM HERE ON *OUT*!

HOLD *ON* TO SOMETHING--KEEP YOUR *WITS*!

WHY DID I CHOOSE *PIRACY*?! I CAN'T EVEN *SWIM*!

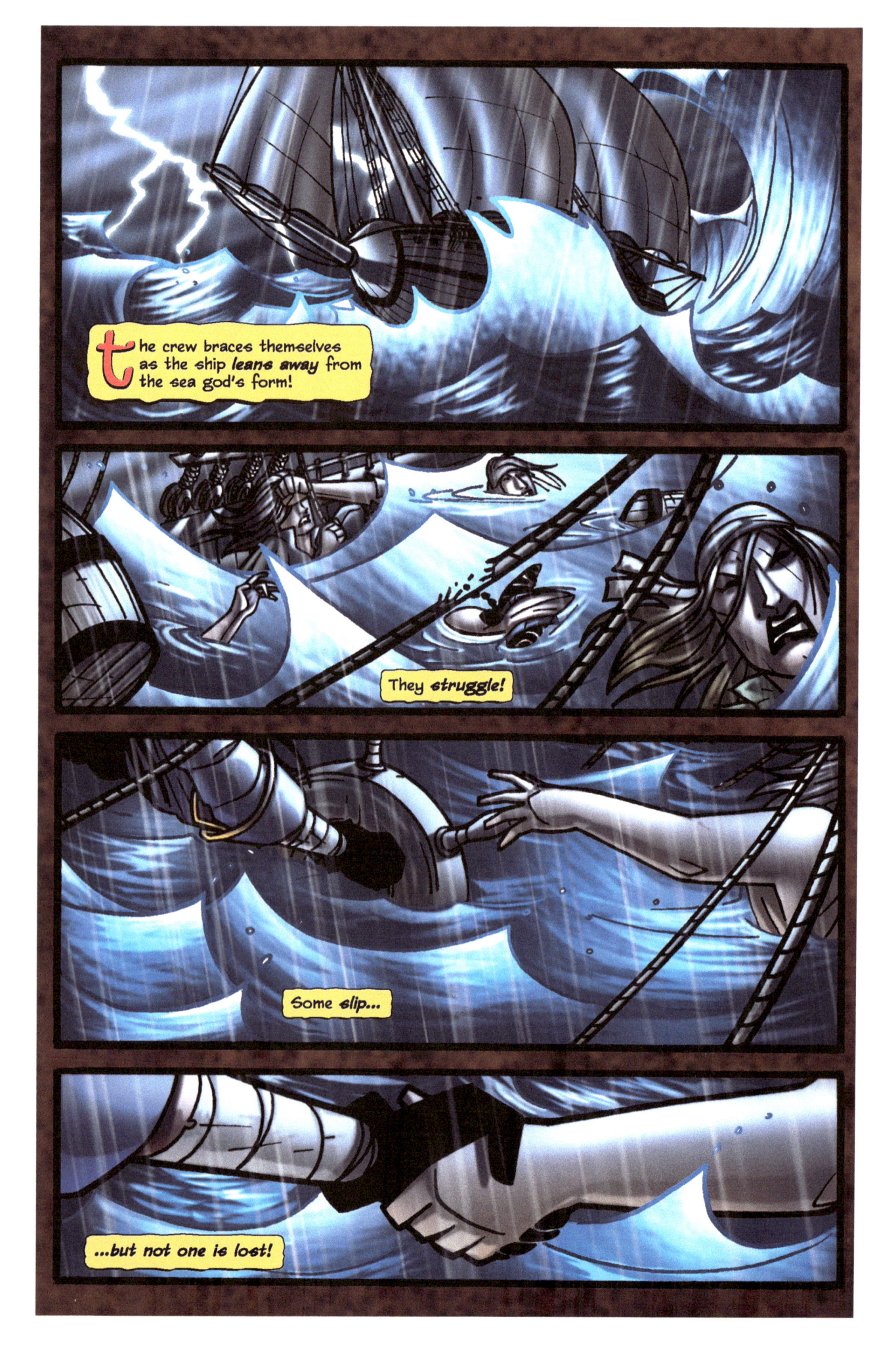

The crew braces themselves as the ship *leans away* from the sea god's form!

They *struggle!*

Some slip...

...but not one is lost!

> **WE CAN'T TAKE ANOTHER HIT LIKE THAT-- IT'LL TEAR US APART!**

> **THERE!**

> **HEAD FOR THE ISLAND--IT'S OUR ONLY WAY OUT!**

> **NEREUS IS GONE FOR NOW, BUT HE'LL BE BACK SOON--AND MORE SWOLLEN THAN EVER!**

> THAT FOOL OF A SEA GOD! THE ONE PLACE HE WAS TRYING TO KEEP ME FROM AND HE LED ME RIGHT TO IT!

DO AS HE SAYS--
--WE'VE GOT NO OTHER OPTIONS AT THE MOMENT!
AYE, CAP'N!
NOW, ROBBIE BUCKLE--WHAT HAVE YOU TO DO WITH THE GODS? WE ALL HEARD YOUR NAME RISING OUT OF THE SEA!
I'M A PATIENT WOMAN, BUT MY PATIENCE IS WEARING THIN...
IT DESIRES A COAT OF EXPLANATIONS!

"IT'S NOT A VERY *EASY* THING TO EXPLAIN, CAPTAIN..."

"*TRY!* I'M NOT TAKING MY CREW THROUGH *HELL* FOR *NOTHING*--"

"--IS THIS TREASURE YOU'VE PROMISED ME *HIS*? DOES IT BELONG TO THE *GOD OF THE SEA*?"

SHE'S GETTING CLOSE TO THE *TRUTH*. I DON'T THINK I CAN KEEP IT FROM HER ANY *LONGER*.

THE TREASURE IS HIS, YES. BUT THAT'S NOT WHY HE CHASES ME.
A MORE *CARNAL* DESIRE DRIVES HIM...
...HE WATCHES ME FROM THE DEPTHS.
HE FOLLOWS ME WHEREVER I SAIL BECAUSE HE CANNOT HAVE ME.

YOU WERE THE LOVER OF NEREUS?
HIS PLAYTHING?
I WAS. AS MUCH AS ONE CAN BE A LOVER TO A GOD. BUT THAT ENDED...
...AND NOW HE CHASES ME--
--DESTROYING WHATEVER AND WHOMEVER I COME IN CONTACT WITH.

"AND THE TREASURE?"

"WE'RE RIGHT ON IT, CAPTAIN..."

"...IT'S BURIED DEEP IN THE CAVES OF THIS ISLAND."

BEST NOT TO TELL HER WHAT ELSE I HAVE HIDDEN ON THE ISLAND.

I'LL JUST KEEP ONE MORE LITTLE THING FROM HER...

I should KILL you where you stand!

You could, and I wouldn't blame you--but first let me show you the TREASURE.

I'm taking MORE than half.

You can have it ALL if we live. There's something ELSE on that island I need.

He takes chances like me. I hate to say it, but I'm starting to respect the little wretch.

the winds pick up once more as the ship nears the island. Nereus readies his mighty self for another attack!

Young Robbie Buckle is intent on beating the sea god. There's a *grievance* to be settled here!

three boats carrying a contingent of the crew make their weary way through the choppy water to the shore. The rest of the crew remain on board the ship...

ALMOST THERE, MATES!

THIS BOAT WON'T BE DRAGGED UNDER WHILE *CAPTAIN HANNA* IS ON BOARD!

AYE, CAP'N!

I WAGER *WE'RE* SAFE--BUT THE OTHERS MIGHT *NOT* BE!

HE'S *BACK!*

WE'RE DONE FOR!

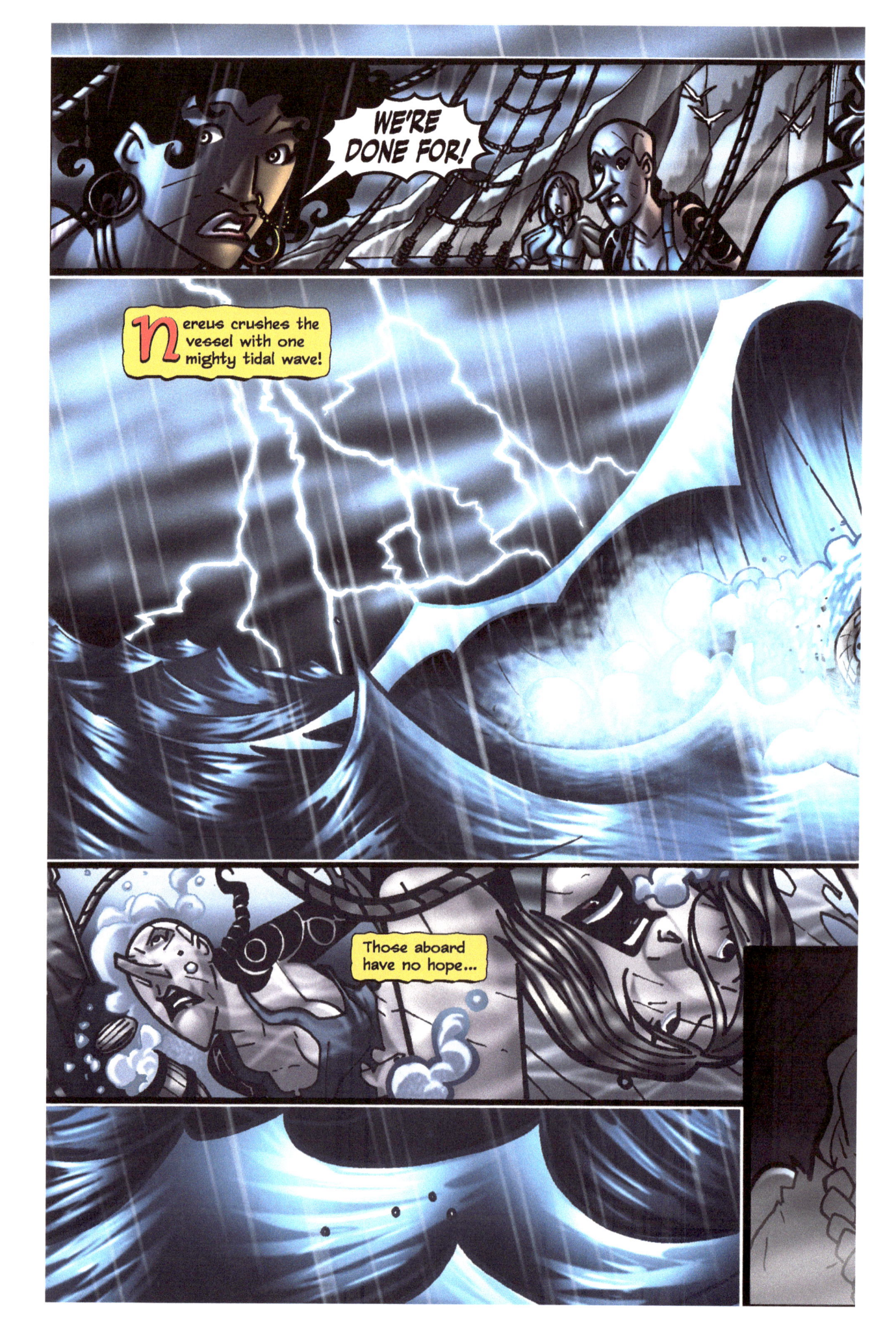

Nereus crushes the vessel with one mighty tidal wave!

Those aboard have no hope...

MY SHIP! MY CREW!

To Be Continued...

Chapter 8

The wrath of the Sea God *Nereus* threatens to submerge the island as Captain Hanna and what's left of her crew follow *Robbie Buckle* into the caves.

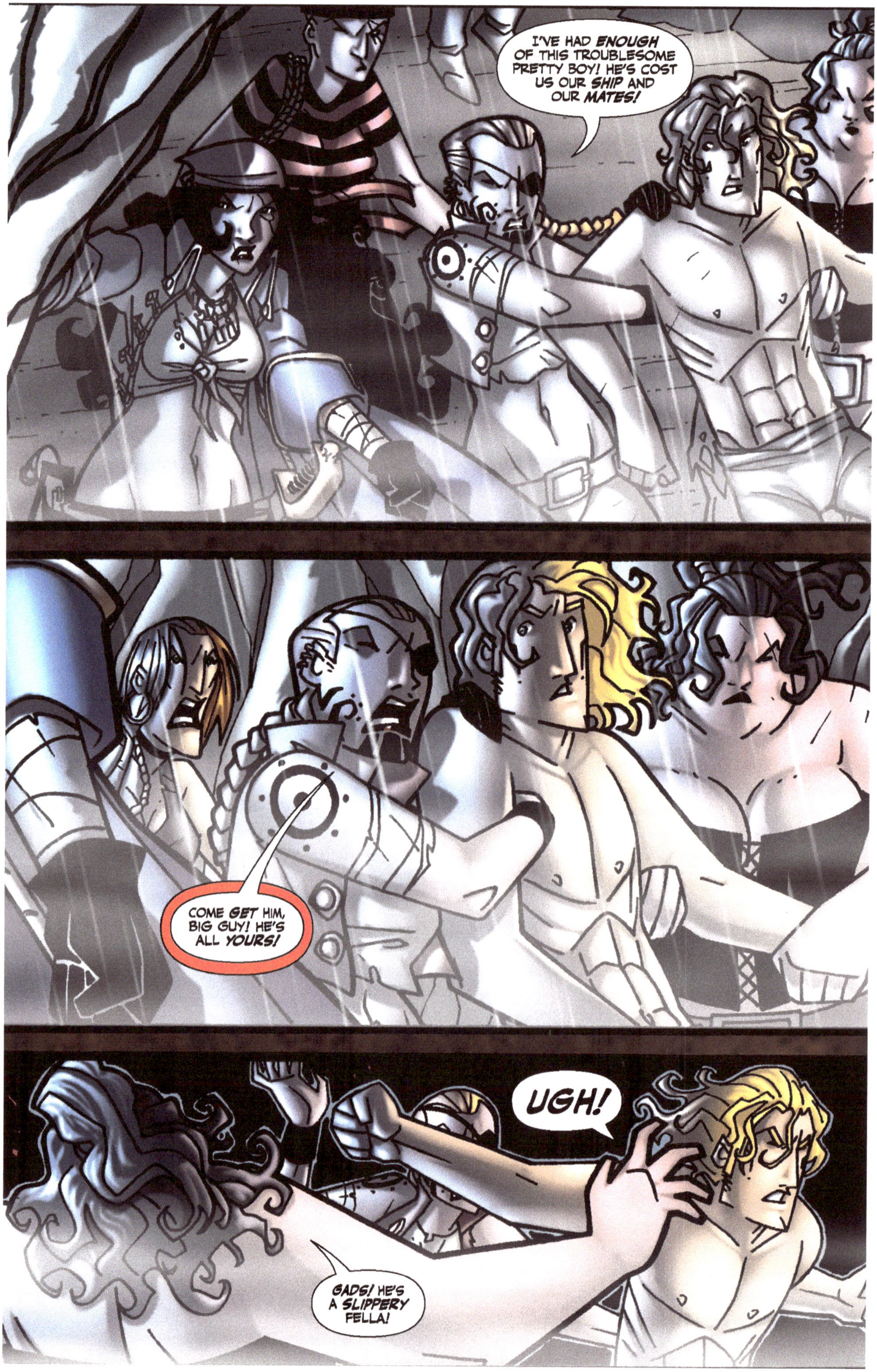
I'VE HAD ENOUGH OF THIS TROUBLESOME PRETTY BOY! HE'S COST US OUR SHIP AND OUR MATES!
COME GET HIM, BIG GUY! HE'S ALL YOURS!
UGH!
GADS! HE'S A SLIPPERY FELLA!

the crew chases Robbie deeper into the caves...

WHAT'S ALL THIS?

WHAT I PROMISED YOU!

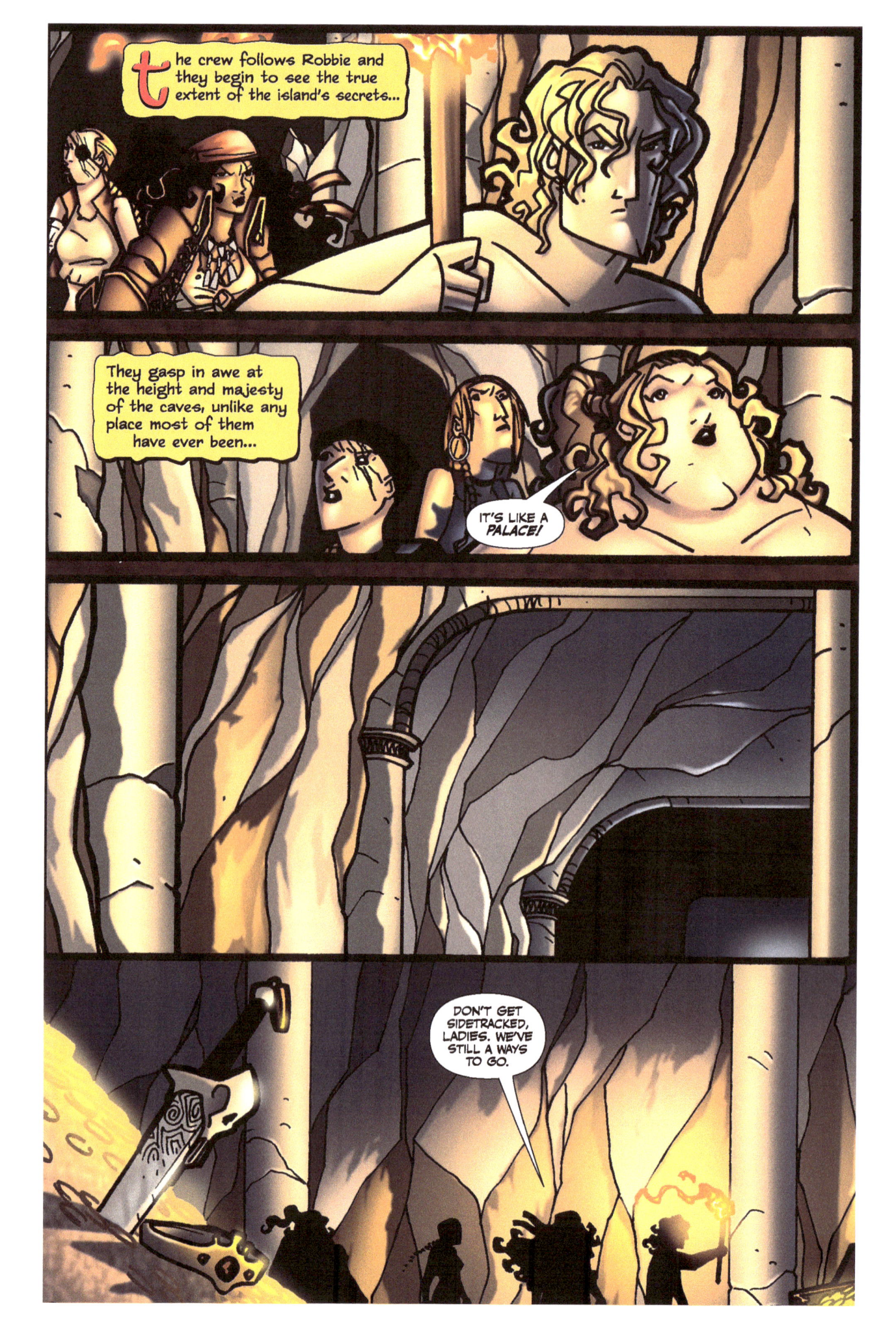

The crew follows Robbie and they begin to see the true extent of the island's secrets...

They gasp in awe at the height and majesty of the caves, unlike any place most of them have ever been...

IT'S LIKE A PALACE!

DON'T GET SIDETRACKED, LADIES. WE'VE STILL A WAYS TO GO.

Meanwhile at sea, *Captain Purloin* spots the island Hanna and her crew have settled on.

THAT STORM BE A FITTING SYMBOL OF MY *WRATH!*

MY MUTINOUS, COWARDLY CREW SHOULD HAVE KNOWN BETTER THAN TO *DEFY* MY ORDERS TO HEAD TO THE ISLAND.

I'LL *HAVE* HANNA AGAIN!

SHE'LL PAY A PRICE *WORTHY* OF MY PRIDE!

On the island, Robbie brings Hanna to the very heart of things...
HERE IT IS, CAPTAIN.
THIS IS THE TREASURE YOU'VE BEEN SEARCHING FOR ALL YOUR *LIFE*, IS IT NOT?
No one says a thing, ***blinded*** by the glittering showcase before them.

But from behind the waterfall appears a *shadow!*

HALT!

WHO'S THERE?

A *man* steps into the light; a man of such silent strength and fortitude that Hanna cannot help but admire him immediately.

THIS WAS ALL A *LOVER'S* QUARREL?
I NEEDED A SHIP.
I'VE BEEN TRYING FOR A *YEAR* TO GET BACK HERE, BUT NEREUS TRIES TO BRING ME INTO HIS DEPTHS AT *EVERY* TURN.

...but she admires her *treasure* even greater.

NOT ANOTHER STEP!

THIS IS *MY* BOUNTY!

I'M AFRAID *YOU'VE* SEEN YOUR LAST DAY.

NO! WAIT!

EXPLAIN YOURSELF, ROBBIE BUCKLE!
THIS IS CASPIAN.
HE IS THE REASON NEREUS CHASES ME.
I REFUSED THE SEA GOD'S ADVANCES TO BE FOREVER WITH CASPIAN.
NEREUS DOES NOT KNOW I HID CASPIAN INSIDE THE ISLAND. BUT I WOULD DEFY AND TRICK A THOUSAND GODS FOR CASPIAN'S LOVE!

HOW SWEET!
I'M GLAD TO HAVE BEEN OF SERVICE.
OUR AID HAS BEEN WELL *PAID* FOR I SUPPOSE.
IT'S ALL YOURS.
TAKE IT.
WHAT GOOD IS THIS TREASURE IF NEREUS SINKS US *WITH* IT ON THIS ISLAND?
YOU'VE LED US TO OUR *DEATHS*, PRETTY BOY!

THERE *IS* A WAY OUT OF THE CAVES. BUT YOU WILL NOT BE ABLE TO TAKE ALL OF THE GOLD AND JEWELS.

THERE'S A WAY FREE WITHOUT BEING SEEN BY NEREUS?

THROUGH THE CAVES, COMING OUT ON THE OTHER SIDE OF THE ISLAND.

I USE IT TO FIND FOOD UP ABOVE.

"YOU HEARD OUR NEW GROWLING FRIEND...

"GRAB WHATEVER YOU CAN CARRY..."

"WE'LL COME BACK LATER WITH A LARGER... *MUCH* LARGER... SHIP."

LEAD THE WAY, HERO!

WHAT'S THE USE OF US LEAVING THE CAVES WITHOUT A SHIP TO *ESCAPE* ON?
ONE DISASTER AT A TIME, MATE.

The sky is thundering overhead as the crew leaves the caves, but the brunt of the storm is focused on the *other* side of the island.

NOW WHAT?

NOW WE WAIT FOR WHATEVER'S NEXT.

hanna spots a familiar and oft *dreaded* vessel approaching the island.

THAT DIDN'T TAKE LONG, AND FOR ONCE I'M *GLAD* FOR IT.

I'VE GOT THE MAKINGS OF A PLAN, MATES!

WHAT'S THIS?

"A POOR LITTLE CAPTAIN, ALL ALONE..."

TOO BAD NO ONE WILL BE AROUND TO SEE YOU DIE!

LOOKS AS IF YOUR CREW HAS DESERTED YOU, HANNA.
A *WORTHIER* CAPTAIN WOULD KNOW HOW TO KEEP THEM IN LINE!
THEY WENT WITH THE SHIP.
AYE! I SPIED THE WRECKAGE.
DON'T WORRY. YOU'LL BE *MEETING* THEM SOON!

As Hanna and Purloin fight on land, Hanna's crew with Robbie and Caspian steal his small landing boat and head for Purloin's vessel with their treasure...

WHAT A MESS! YOU'RE GOING TO HAVE SOME *WORK* TO DO.

UGH!
YOU'RE GETTING WEAK IN YOUR OLD AGE, PURLOIN...
Those waves are getting high, and the winds are getting mighty strong.
I hope I can make it back on the ship in time...

ROBBIE! LOOK!
ANYONE FOR SACRIFICING THEMSELVES FOR THE GOOD OF OTHERS?
The End...for now...

Chapter 9

Dead or Alive

SOMEWHERE OFF THE COAST OF AFRICA

"THE LOBSTERS WERE SWARMING. THEY WERE ALL OVER ME ARSE!"

"BUT ONE BE ONE, I BUSTED THEIR BARNACLES!"

"SENDING THEM TO DAVY TO SAY A HELLO."

"THE MAGISTRATE'S MUG WAS FLABBERGASTED."

"HE WAS BEING ROBBED IN BROAD DAYLIGHT AND NOT A THING TO DO ABOUT IT."

"THE CARGO WAS A KING'S RANSOM, FOR THREE AT BEST."

"GOLD, SILVER, AND JADE, ALL PRIED FROM THE DEAD HANDS OF SAVAGES."

"THEN I, LADIES, THE GREAT DRAKE SANTAGO, SPLIT WITH THE RICHES."

"IT WAS A BEAUTY!"

"Why that wig even put a 5,000 schilling bounty on me head."

"Surprised he had that left."

"Oh Santago, you so dangerous."

"We like dangerous."

"Dangerous makes for fun."

"Well blow me down... If ye not careful ladies, I be robbing ye of your buried treasure."

GRANTED, YE BOOTY LOOKS TO BE PLUNDERED.
BUT OL' DRAKE CAN FIND SOME JEWEL.
YOU TALK TO MUCH. DRINK.
-HIC!-
NOT...
FEEL...
SO GOOD...

"I CAN'T... MOVE..."

"THAT WOULD BE THE POISON."

"A SINGAPORE COCKTAIL, MY SPECIALTY."

"POISON?"

"YES, MAKES BIG MEN LIMP."

"RATHER HARMLESS."

"UNLIKE THIS!"

BAM
BAM
GAK!
SPLAT SPLAT
BLIMEY...
SORRY FOR THE CLOSE CALL.
I HAD TO CONFIRM MY MARK.

WHO...

WHO ARE YOU?

HOW RUDE.

THE NAME IS MORGAN.

MORGAN "HACK" SHEPPARD.

BOUNTY HUNTER.

OH.

AND THIS IS MAO JIN.

CHINESE WITCHCRAFT PSYCHOPATH.

JIN HERE HAS MURDERED BUCKS AND BLOKES ALL ACROSS THE ROAMING SEAS.

SHE WAS LOOKING TO CUT OFF YE BOLLOCKS FOR THE SUPERNATURAL MUMBO-JUMBO.

LUCKY YE ARE.

I ALSO KNOW YOU'RE NOT DRAKE SANTAGO, SEÑOR IMPOSTER.
IMPOSTER?
WHAT... WHAT DO YE MEAN?
DRAKE SANTAGO IS NEARLY SEVEN FEET TALL AND AFRICAN.
HE IS AS BLACK AS IVORY IS NOT.
A REAL FIERCE SON-OF-A-BITCH.
PUT UP A HELL OF A FIGHT HE DID.
LEAST TILL MY PARTNER SHOT HIM DEAD.
AND THE BOUNTY WAS 6,000 SCHILLINGS, NOT 5,000.

YOU SHOULD REALLY BE MORE CAREFUL WHO YE FANCY YOURSELF.
SOME OF ME CONTEMPORARIES ARE NOT AS ON THE UPPITY-UP AS I.
NOR FORGIVING.
CHOP

YOU WERE RIGHT PATRICK.

IT WAS HER.

SHE WENT AFTER THAT DAGO LIKE A SHARK AFTER HIS CHUM.

GOOD WORK LASS.
YOU'RE THE BEST.
YE KNOW, I STILL THINK YE SHOULD HAVE DONE THIS JOB.
NAH LASS.
YOU HAD THIS ALL THE WAY.
BESIDES, I WOULD HAVE NEVER BEEN ABLE TO PULL OFF THOSE TASSELS.
OF COURSE YOU COULD DARLING.
YE WOULD LOOK FABULOUS.
COME ON. LETS SHOVE OF THIS ROCK.
THAT MELON WILL BE ROTTEN RIPE. THE BRITS ARE NOT FRENCH, AND DON'T PAY EXTRA FOR STENCH.

THE BARREL DRAGONS, GIBRALTAR.

GREAT WORK! THE GOVERNOR LOVED THE NEW ORNAMENT.

HE LOVED IT SO MUCH HE'S GOT ANOTHER ONE FOR YOU CUTTHROATS.

I'M GLAD TO HEAR THAT, FRANCIS.

WHAT'S THE NEXT JOB? I HATE IDLING.

AND I HATE ZOMBIES. IT BETTER NOT BE A ZOMBIE HUNT.

"NO MORGAN, NO ZOMBIES."

"THE MARK LIVES AND BREATHES, A POWDER KEG, FULL O' SPIT AND VINEGAR."

"A REAL DEVIL OF A PIRATE."

"HANNA TEACH, SPAWN OF BLACKBEARD."

"THAT'S LOVELY."

"NOW GET TO THE PART I LIKE."

"HOW MUCH FOR THE HEAD?"

"OH, IT'S BIG, REAL BIG. A HUNDRED THOUSAND POUNDS BIG."

"A HUNDRED THOUSAND POUNDS! MUST BE PERSONAL."

"BY THE DOG'S BOLLOCKS IT IS. LET'S JUST SAY SHE CAN BE A REAL HEARTBREAKER."

"SO WHERE DO WE FIND THIS HANNA TEACH?"

"TRUTHFULLY, MY MEMORY IS AT BEST BIT FOGGY. PERHAPS ANOTHER DRINK WOULD HELP GIVE SOME CLARITY."

"I'LL GET YA DRINK. BUT THAT MEMORY BEST BE SPILLING ITS GUTS."

"OR I'LL BE SPILLING IT FOR YA."

"SHE ALWAYS THIS CHARMING, OR DOES SHE JUST LIKE ME?"

"SHE LIKES YOU."

"NOW, YOU WERE ABOUT TO SAY."

WHAT CAN I GET THE LOVELY LADY?
A BLACKJACK FILLED WITH YOUR STRONGEST.
MAKE THAT A PAIR.
EXCUSE ME, ARE YOU LOST?
I BELIEVE THE WHOREHOUSE IS ACROSS THE WAY.
LUCKY YE ARE THEY'RE HIRING.
WELL HOLY BOUNCING CANNON-BALLS!
WHY IT'S PHAHED AND SHARAH. FOR A PAIR OF NOTORIOUSLY SECOND RATE BOUNTY HUNTERS, YOU GUYS ALWAYS MADE A LOVELY COUPLE.
CAREFUL WITH YOU WORDS GIRL!
I'VE ALWAYS FOUND THAT THE SMARTEST ASSES HAS THE TASTIEST BRAINS.

WHAT YOU GUYS WANT, BESIDES EATING MY BRAINS OF COURSE?

I RECOGNIZED YOUR EXISTENCE. ISN'T THAT ENOUGH FOR ONE DAY? NOW GO ON YOUR WAY.

WHAT WE WANT IS RESPECT! WE BEEN IN THIS BUSINESS AS LONG AS YOU AND YOUR ONE-EYED GOON. DELIVERED JUST AS MANY HEADS.

AND WHAT DO WE GET FOR OUR TROUBLES. SCRAPS! SCRAPS OF RESPECT.

WELL IF YOU SPENT LESS TIME SLAUGHTERING ORPHANS AND URCHINS, YE MIGHT GET MORE RESPECT.

HOW MANY WAS IT?

FIFTY, SIXTY?

THAT WAS ONE TIME!

BESIDES, THEY WERE A MENACE. ALWAYS BEGGING FOR MONEY.

OH BUGGER OFF! MOST THOSE PUPS WERE ONLY THREE YEARS YOUNG.

SHARAH HERE ATE A HALF DOZEN OF THEM.

HEY! I ONLY ATE THREE.

THE REST WERE ALL SKIN AND BONE. NOT EVEN PROPER FOR A STEW.

SILENCE!

WE'RE HERE ON A PROFESSIONAL COURTESY, A WARNING MORE TO THE POINT.

YOU REMEMBER THAT LITTLE INCIDENT IN JAMAICA. I'M SURE YOU DO.

REGARDLESS, YOU EARNED YOURSELF QUITE A PRICE ON YOUR HEAD.

A CHEST FULL OF SPANISH GOLD AS A MATTER OF FACT.

WHY THERE IS EVEN A BONUS FOR YOUR PARTNER.

CAN YOU IMAGINE OUR EXCITEMENT? ELIMINATE OUR RIVALS AND BATH IN THE RICHES OF KINGS!

WELL PHAHED, I'D LIKE TO THANK YOU FOR YOUR PROFESSIONAL COURTESY.

IN ADDITION, LET ME EXTEND MY OWN PROFESSIONAL COURTESY AND BE THE FIRST TO WISH YOU A BOUNTIFUL AMOUNT OF--

GOOD LUCK!
POW!
YEAH!
WATCH IT!
SLAM
YE BLOODY OAF!
YE SPILT ME MATE'S DRINK.
YEAH, YE SPILT ME DRINK.
YE BEST BE PAYING FOR THAT.
PAYING WITH PAIN!
OH THERE BE PAYING ALRIGHT!

BLOODY!
I'M GONNA SUCK THE MORROW FROM YOU'RE PRETTY BONES!
I GOT TWO KNUCKLE CLUSTERS THAT SAY OTHERWISE!
CRACK
SORRY PATRICK, BUT IT HAD TO BE DONE.
WE GOT OUR LEAD?
SURE DO LASS. WE NEED TO FIND A BOAT AND PASSAGE.
WHERE TO?
MADA-GASCAR...

"THE PIRATE DEN THEY CALL ST. MARY'S."

CAPTAIN?

BEG A THOUSAND PARDONS, BUT WE JUST NOT PORT FOR RUM AND LIMEYS.
NAH CHIN. THERE IS MORE HERE TO DO THEN STOCKING THE GALLEY.
THIS CITY IS OLD.
A CITY BUILT BY LONG DEAD KINGS.
KINGS BURIED DEEP UNDER THESE STONES.
AND WHERE THERE ARE DEAD KINGS, THERE BE DEAD KING'S TREASURE.
I AIM TO FIND THESE GRAVES AND GIVE THEM A GOOD ROBBING.

BUT FOR NOW STOCK UP ON THESE GREEN NUGGETS. I TIRE OF THE CREW WHINING OF SCURVY.
CAP'N. CAP'N LOOK, LOOK AT THE POST.
THE PICTURE CAP'N. LONG DARK HAIR, SCAR UNDER EYE, AMPLE BOSOM.
THAT YOU CAP'N.
WANTED DEAD
HANNA TEACH

100,000 POUNDS. WHY CAPTAIN, THOUGHT YOU WORTH TWICE THAT.
WANTED
DEAD DARREN DAVIS
ESPECIALLY FOR THIS LIST.
PIRACY, MURDER, ASSAULT, ROBBERY, BURGLARY, ARSON, BLACKMAIL, VANDALISM, THEFT, TRAFFICKING, BRIBERY, MANSLAUGHTER--
WHAT? MANSLAUGHTER! WHY I NEVER KILL'T ANYONE I DIDN'T AIM TOO.
LEAST THE LIKENESS IS GOOD.
FUNNY. I HAVE TO DISAGREE.
YOU MUCH UGLIER IN PERSON, MISS TEACH.
MISS TEACH, HOW FORMAL.
YOU SEEM TO HAVE ME AT A DISADVANTAGE, MISS...?
MORGAN SHEPPARD.
BOUNTY HUNTER.
I'M HERE FOR YOUR HEAD.
TO BE CONTINUED...

Chapter 10

"Will you hear of a bloody battle...
"...lately fought upon the seas?
UGNH!
BLAM
BLAM
BLAM
"It will make your ears to rattle...
BOOM
APPARENTLY, CAP'N, THESE LOBSTERBACKS HAVEN'T A CLUE AS TO WHO THEY'RE DEALING WITH.
"...and our admiration cease."

THEN IT WOULD SEEM, MISTER MACPHERSON...
...'TWAS HIGH TIME I INTRODUCED MYSELF!
AYE, CAP'N HANNA.
THAT IT WOULD.
BLAM
BOOM
BLAM
BLAM
BLAM
MAKE WAY, YE HEARTY FOOLS...

...FOR THE DAUGHTER O' BLACKBEARD!
BLAM
YER NOT EXACTLY THE CREAM OF HIS MAJESTY'S CROP...
KRUKT
...ARE YA?
BRACKT
NOW, THAT'S DOWNRIGHT OFFENSIVE, MISTER...
YOU TRULY ARE CUT FROM THE SAME CLOTH AS YOUR FATHER.

MONTGOMERY. I'M WHAT YOU MIGHT CALL... A FRIEND OF THE FAMILY.

WELL, SINCE I GOT A FAMILY FULLA' FREAKS, YE CERTAINLY FILL THE BILL.

HOWEVER, ALL THINGS BEIN' EQUAL...

...I'D RATHER CALL YE A LOBSTER-CLAWED, LOBSTERBACK LOON.

BLAM SKRAZT BLAM SKRAZT BLAM

NO OFFENSE.

SPLASH
ENOUGH!
BLAM
BLAM
BLAM
SAVE YOUR POWDER.
THE HAUGHTY HANNA TEACH IS NO MORE.
T'WOULD SEEM THE LIEUTENANT IS CORRECT.
T'WOULD ALSO APPEAR...
...THE WENCH TRULY IS HOLIER THAN THOU --
--NOW.
SHALL WE CONTINUE WITH THE CANNONS OR PREPARE TO BOARD?
NEITHER, SERGEANT DEPP.
THIS SKIRMISH HAS LITTLE TO DO WITH OUR MISSION.
AND, IN ALL HONESTY, I WOULD LIKE TO FINISH THIS...
...MYSELF.

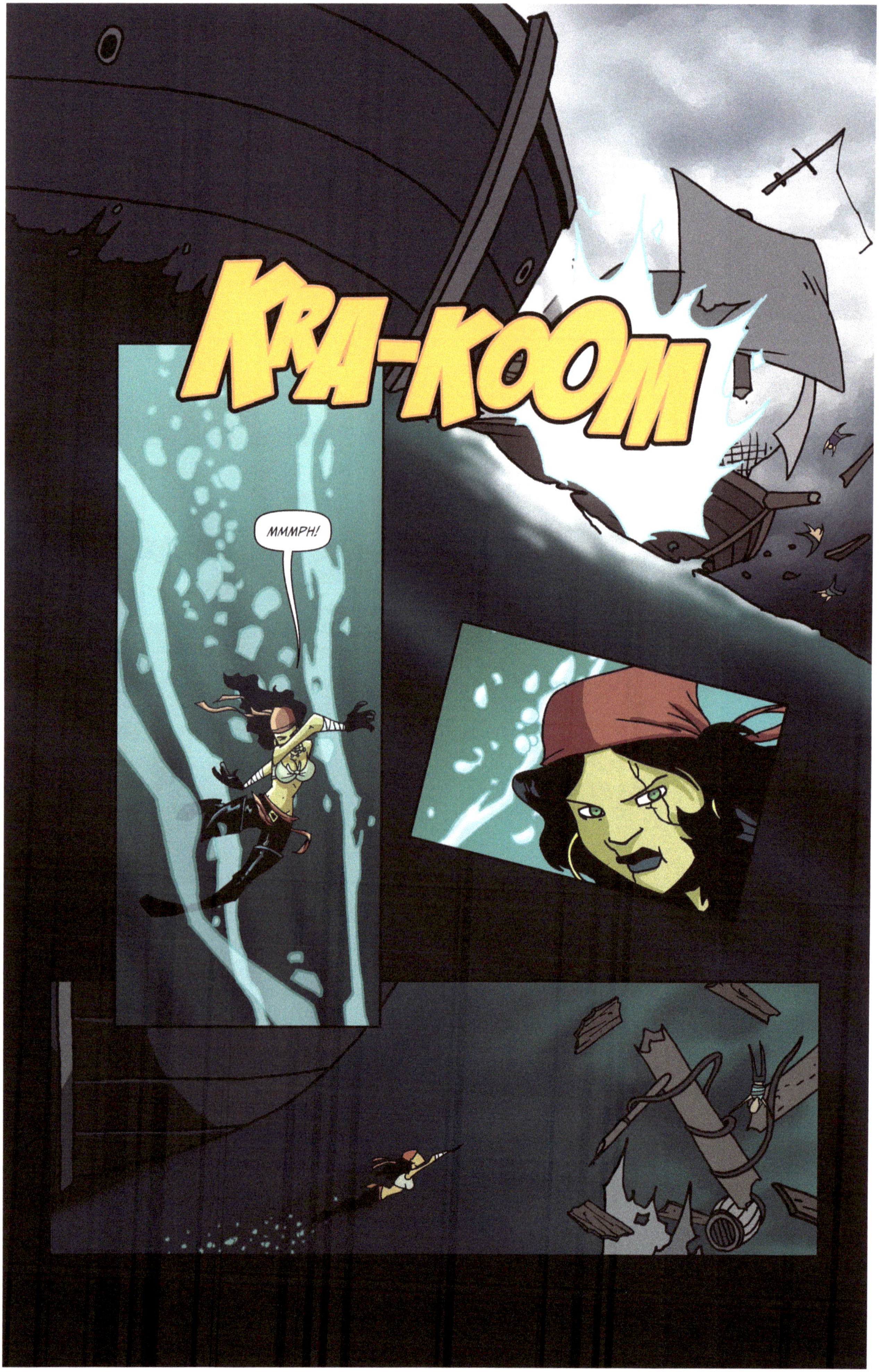
KRA-KOOM
MMMPH!

GASP!

NO... MY CREW--

--MY SHIP...

BEGIN THE CONVERSION.

YOU *HEARD* THE LIEUTENANT. AVERY AND MILLER, MAN THE ROTATOR.

EVERYONE ELSE, TO YOUR STATIONS AND *READY* THE INFLATABLE.

UNNGH.

SPLUSH
HAVE TO FIND A WAY--
SPLUSH
--TO BOARD THIS BLASTED BOAT AND...
...THAT'LL DO.
"Have you heard of teach the rover and his knavery on the main?
"how, of gold, he was a lover; how he loved all ill-got gain?"

"When the act of grace appeared, captain teach, with all his men...

"...unto Carolina steered, where they kindly us'd him then."

'TIS ODD FOR THE STREETS TO BE SO PEACEFUL...

...IN A TIME OF WAR.

WHAT IS IT, FRIEND? WHAT HAVE YOU SEEN?

SKREEE

DYANI, WHILE I MORE THAN ADMIRE YOUR PEOPLE'S AMAZING CULTURE...

...I FIND IT UTTERLY IMPROBABLE THAT YOU CAN ACTUALLY COMMUNICATE WITH THESE CREATURES.

DID YOU NOT MAKE THE MAGIC GUN ON PISTOLFIST'S ARM, DOCTOR FRANKLIN?

No newline at end of file

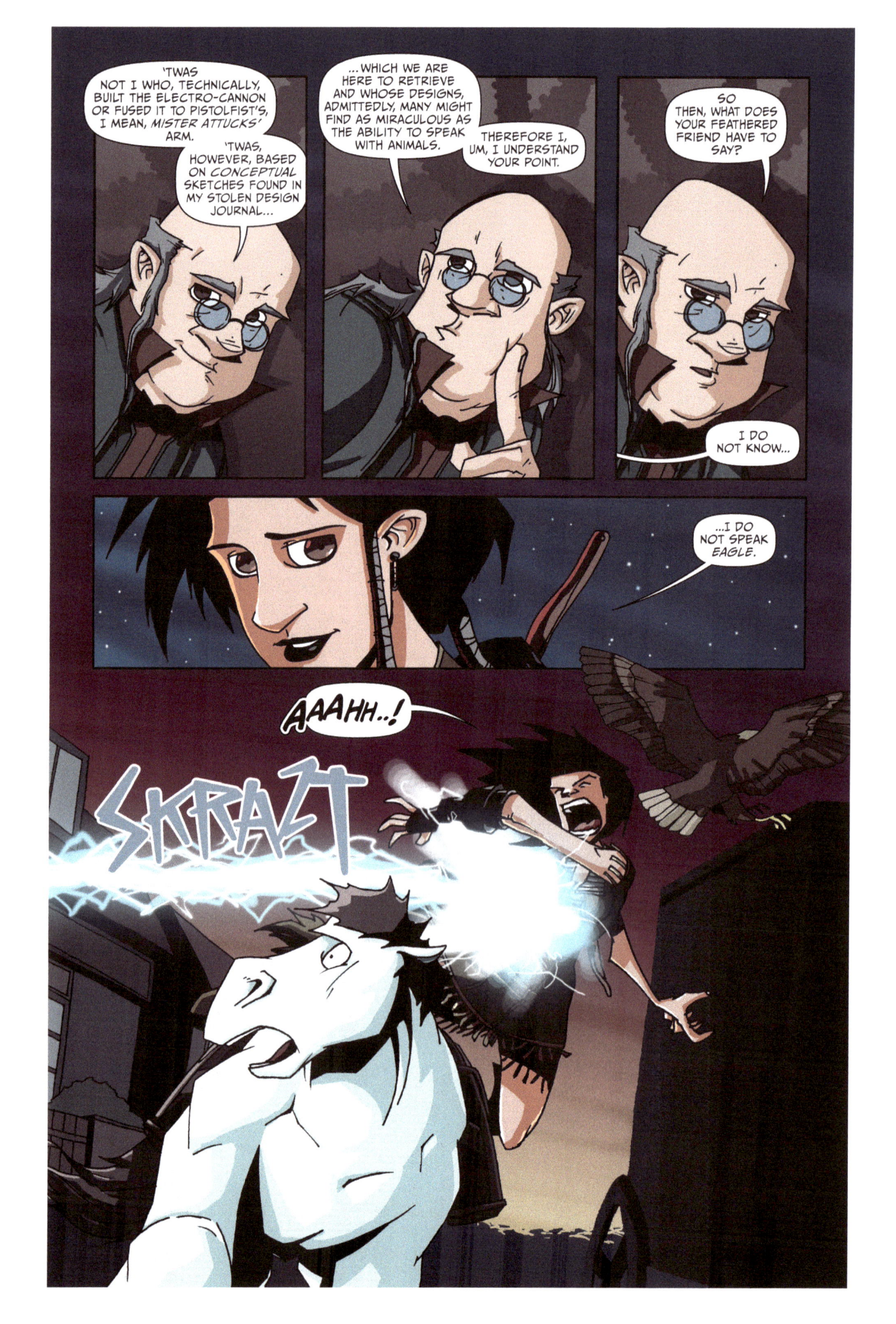

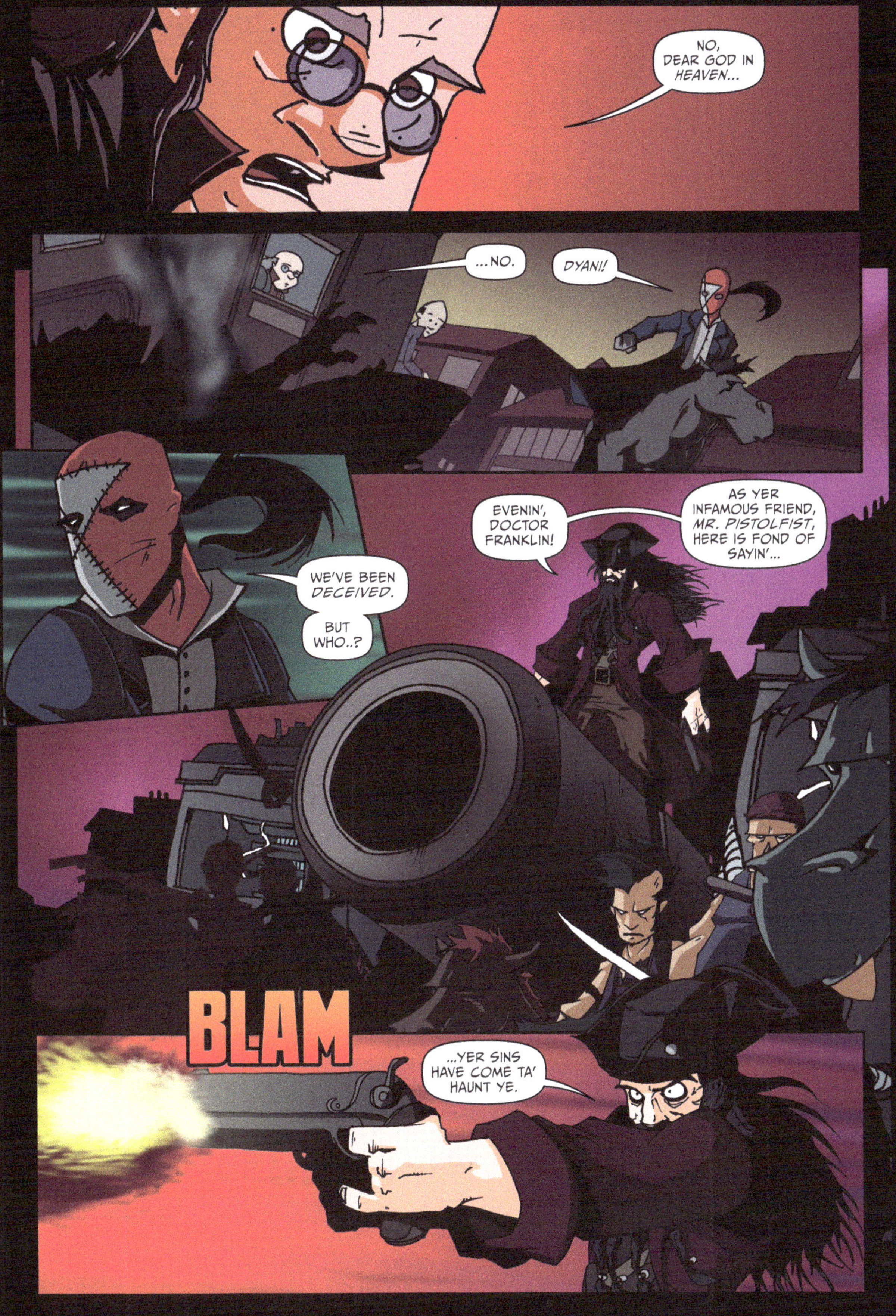

NO, DEAR GOD IN HEAVEN...
...NO.
DYANI!
WE'VE BEEN DECEIVED.
BUT WHO..?
EVENIN', DOCTOR FRANKLIN!
AS YER INFAMOUS FRIEND, MR. PISTOLFIST, HERE IS FOND OF SAYIN'...
BLAM
...YER SINS HAVE COME TA' HAUNT YE.

NNGH...
'TIS A *TRAP*, DOCTOR!
GET TO A PLACE OF SAFETY!
SKRAZT
AND JUST WHERE, PRAY TELL, WOULD *THAT* BE?!
BRAKHOOM
AAAUGH!
I'VE TAKEN OUT THE POWER TO THEIR CANNON!
NOW FLY, DOCTOR...
...FLY LIKE AN EAGLE!
OF COURSE.
KLIKT

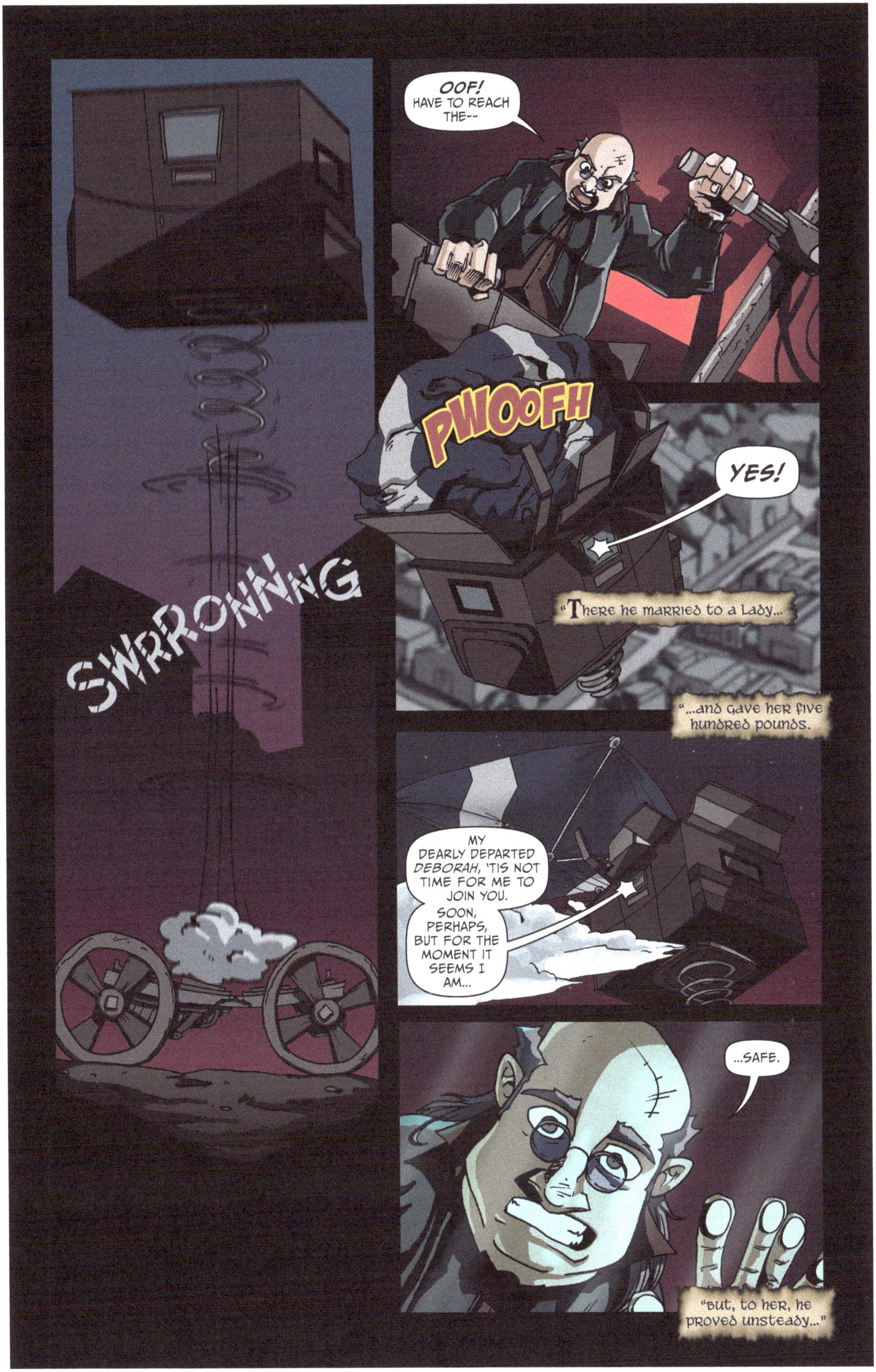
OOF! HAVE TO REACH THE--
PWOOFH
YES!
SWRRONNNG
"There he married to a Lady...
"...and gave her five hundred pounds.
MY DEARLY DEPARTED DEBORAH, 'TIS NOT TIME FOR ME TO JOIN YOU.
SOON, PERHAPS, BUT FOR THE MOMENT IT SEEMS I AM...
...SAFE.
"But, to her, he proved unsteady..."

"For he soon marched off the ground.

"and returned, as I tell you, to his robbery as before.

"burning, sinking ships of value, filling them with purple gore."

WAIT, I KNOW THAT EMBLEM-- 'TIS THE JOLLY ROGER OF EDWARD TEACH HIMSELF!
THEN... THEN THAT WOULD MEAN BLACKBEARD IS STILL ALIVE AND--
--HERE TA' SETTLE A DEBT THAT'S LONG PAST-DUE.
YE SHOULD CEASE YER FIGHTIN' AN' JOIN US.
'TIS NO PLACE IN THE COLONIES FER A RUNAWAY SLAVE.
SKRAZT
UHNN
BLAM BLAM
NGH
SADLY, THY ACTIONS BETRAY THY WORDS.

KRACKT

UNHHH...

THEY'RE HEADED FOR OCRACOKE ISLE...

...THE LAIR O' THAT DEVIL BLACKBEARD AN' HIS RED-COATED ROGUES.

'TIS WHERE WE'RE HEADED AS WELL.

TO MURDER THE MONSTERS WHO *BUTCHERED* OUR MEN.

"When he was at carolina, there the governor did send...

"...to the governor of Virginia, that he might assistance lend."

THEN, I SHALL *JOIN* YOU...

...AFTER I HONOR MY FRIEND.

"THEN THE MAN-O-WAR'S COMMANDER, TWO SMALL SLOOPS HE FITTED OUT...

"...FIFTY MEN HE PUT ON BOARD, SIR, WHO *RESOLVED* TO STAND IT OUT.

"VALIANT MAYNARD AS HE SAILED, SOON THE *PIRATE* DID ESPY...

"...WITH HIS TRUMPET HE THEN HAILED, AND TO HIM THEY DID REPLY..."

"THE LIEUTENANT HE COMMANDED BOTH THE SLOOPS, AND YOU SHALL HEAR...

"...HOW, BEFORE HE LANDED, HE SUPPRESSED THEM WITHOUT FEAR.

"...CAP'N TEACH IS OUR COMMANDER...
"...MAYNARD SAID, 'E IS THE MAN...
...WHOM I AM RESOLVED TA' HANG..."
"...LET 'IM DO THE BEST 'E CAN.
"TEACH REPLIED UNTO MAYNARD, YE NO QUARTER HERE SHALL SEE...
"...BUT BE HANGED ON THE *MAINYARD*, YE AND ALL YER COMPANY."
'TIS MY FAVORITE PART.
SURELY, THOU ART JOKING.
OH, NO... THE MERE MENTION OF A HANGIN' SETS ME HEART ALL A FLUTTER.
NO, I MEAN... 'TIS WHAT ALL THIS RUCKUS IS *ABOUT?*
A POEM I CRAFTED WHEN I WAS BUT A *LAD?!*
'TWOULD SEEM A BIT...

...DRASTIC.
NO ONE MAKES A MOCKERY O' BLACKBEARD!
NOT SOME IGNORANT SCHOOLBOY, DA' BLOODY KING O' ENGLAND OR AN INCOMPETENT IGNORAMUS LIKE MAYNARD!
THAT'S WHAT THIS BE ALL 'BOUT!!
BUT... THEN WHY ALIGN THYSELF WITH THESE BRITISH SOLDIERS? SURELY HIS MAJESTY--
--HAS FORSAKEN' 'EM THE SAME WAY HE DONE ME AND ME MEN.
I, ON THE OTHER HAND, OFFER'D 'EM FREEDOM... TRUE FREEDOM... NOT THE KIND YE COLONIAL CRYBABIES WHIMPER FER.
Fount o' Youth
FREEDOM O' THE DEEP BLUE WATER AN' THE HEAVENS HIGH ABOVE.
I DARE SAY THE PLACE YER HEADIN' WILL BLISTER YER BRITCHES A BIT MORE 'N HEAVEN...
...DADDY DEAREST!
"Maynard said, I none desire of such knaves as thee and thine."

"None I'll give, teach then replyed, my boys give me a glass of wine.
AAAAH... ME DARLIN' DAUGHTER, HANNA...
YE GOT ME.
"he took the glass and drank damnation, unto maynard and his crew...
"...to himself and generation, then the glass away he threw.
SHE KILL'D THE CAP'N!
"brave maynard was resolved to have him...
BLAM
BLAM
BLAM
"...though he'd cannons nine or ten."

"Teach a broadside quickly gave him...
GOODNESS!
KRINK
WATCH THE BLOODY BATTERY...
...YOU FOOLS!
WSSSSS
"...killing sixteen valiant men."
KABOOMAH

WHOMMP WHUMP POK POK

"Maynard boarded him, and to it they fell with sword and pistol, too...

UHHH...

"...they had courage, and did show it, killing of the pirate's crew."

S-SALEM?

SLIDE DOWN THE ANCHOR LINES!
"Teach and maynard on the quarter...
"...fought it out most manfully.
"maynard's sword did cut him shorter..."
I DOUBT THIS LASS OR I WILL MAKE IT DOWN THE ANCHOR LINES.
THEN GET HER INSIDE THAT FLYING BOX...
...NOW!
SPLASH
RAAURH!
SKRAZT
SKRAZT

"...Losing his head...
I ONCE HATED YOU FOR MURDERING MY BROTHER.
NOW, I PITY THE MONSTER YOU'VE BECOME.
SKRAKT
"...he there did die.
NOOOOO!
SNAP
SNAP
SNAP
"every sailor fought while he, sir, power had to wield the sword...
HERE, SALEM!
"...not a coward could you see, sir...
...fear was driven from abroad."
KRAKAKOOM

I-I CAN'T DO IT!
YOU'RE SLIPPING!!
"Wounded men on both sides fell, sir 'twas a doleful sight to see...
"...nothing could their courage quell, sir, o' they fought courageously.
I'D *HUFF* LIKE TO INTRODUCE HANNA, DAUGHTER...
-- AND SLAYER *HUFF* OF BLACKBEARD, THE BEAST BEHIND ALL OF THIS.
"when the bloody fight was over, we're informed by a letter writ...
UNFORTUNATELY, FATHER'S SURVIVED FAR WORSE THAN A BLADE TA' THE GUT.
BUT I HOPE AN' PRAY YER RIGHT, DOCTOR...
"...teach's head was made a cover, to the jack staff of the ship.
...FER ALL OUR SAKES.
"thus they sailed to virginia, and when they the story told, how they kill'd the pirates many, they'd applause from young and old."
Fount o' youth
"The Downfall of Piracy" by
Benjamin Franklin, age 12

Chapter 11

CLICK

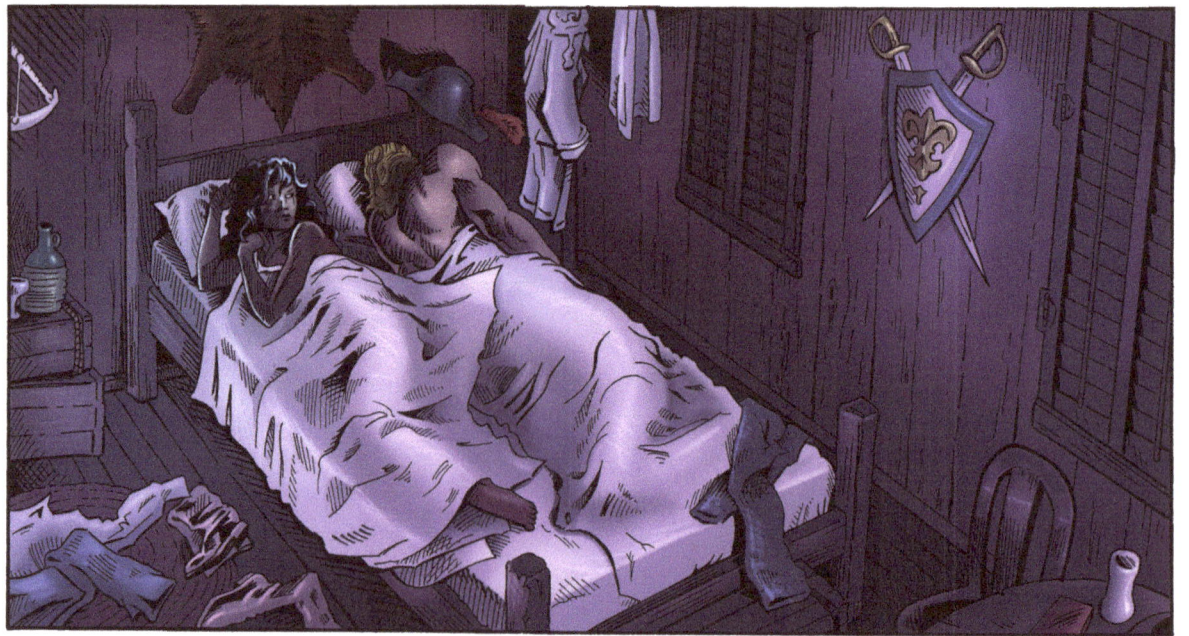

IT IS AN ISLAND OF PIRATES, CUTTHROATS, AND THIEVES... BUT AREN'T THOSE THREE THINGS REALLY THE SAME?
MIGHT QUICKLY WAN' EXPLAIN TA' ME WHY YER FLITTERING ABOUT AT NIGHT, LITTLE BIRD.
I... I WAS LOOKING FOR MA' HAIR BRUSH. I JUST WANTED TO FRESHEN MA' HAIR UP AND CLIMB BACK IN BED. IT'S A MAIDEN THING.
IT'S NOT THE FIRST TIME HANNAH HAS LIED TO A MAN AND IT WON'T BE THE LAST... TONIGHT EVEN.

HOW 'CANNA KNOW YOU AINT HIDING A DAGGER HEADED FOR ME THROAT?
SHBOOP
NOW CAN YA' TELL I'M UNARMED.
I SAPPOS' YER RIGHT.
STIKT
I CAN SHOW YA' MY DAGGER.
THIS ONE?!
SEEN IT! NOT IMPRESSED!

STOLE THE BOOK. KICKED THE PENIS. EXIT CASUALLY.
BLAM
$#!+!!!
STOP THAT WENCH!!!
WENCH?!
HOW OUTDATED...
AND OFFENSIVE!
NOT ZO FAST WENCH.
SERIOUSLY?

LET ME GUESS. BOUNTY HUNTER?
I'VE SHANKED MANY BOUNTY HUNTERS IN MY DAYS, BUT ON POSEIDON'S NAME, YER CERTAINLY THE PRETTIEST.
CLANG
ZIT IZ A COMMON MISCONCEPTION THAT ALL BOUNTY HUNTAZ ARE UGLY MEN.

ALLOW ME TO INTRODUCE MYSELF. I'M HANNAH, DAUGHTER OF CAPTAIN BLACKBEARD. I'M SWEET AS JAMAICAN SUGAR AND ON A JOURNEY TO A FORTUNE YA COULDN'T EVEN DREAM OF.
WANTED
FORTUNE? ZAT SOUNDS INTERESTING.
IT WILL BE A BIGGA' HAUL THAN MY FATHER EVER LAID HIS DIRTY HANDS ON...
AND I'M CURRENTLY IN THE MARKET FOR A FIRST MATE. BONUS POINTS IF SHE'S HOT.

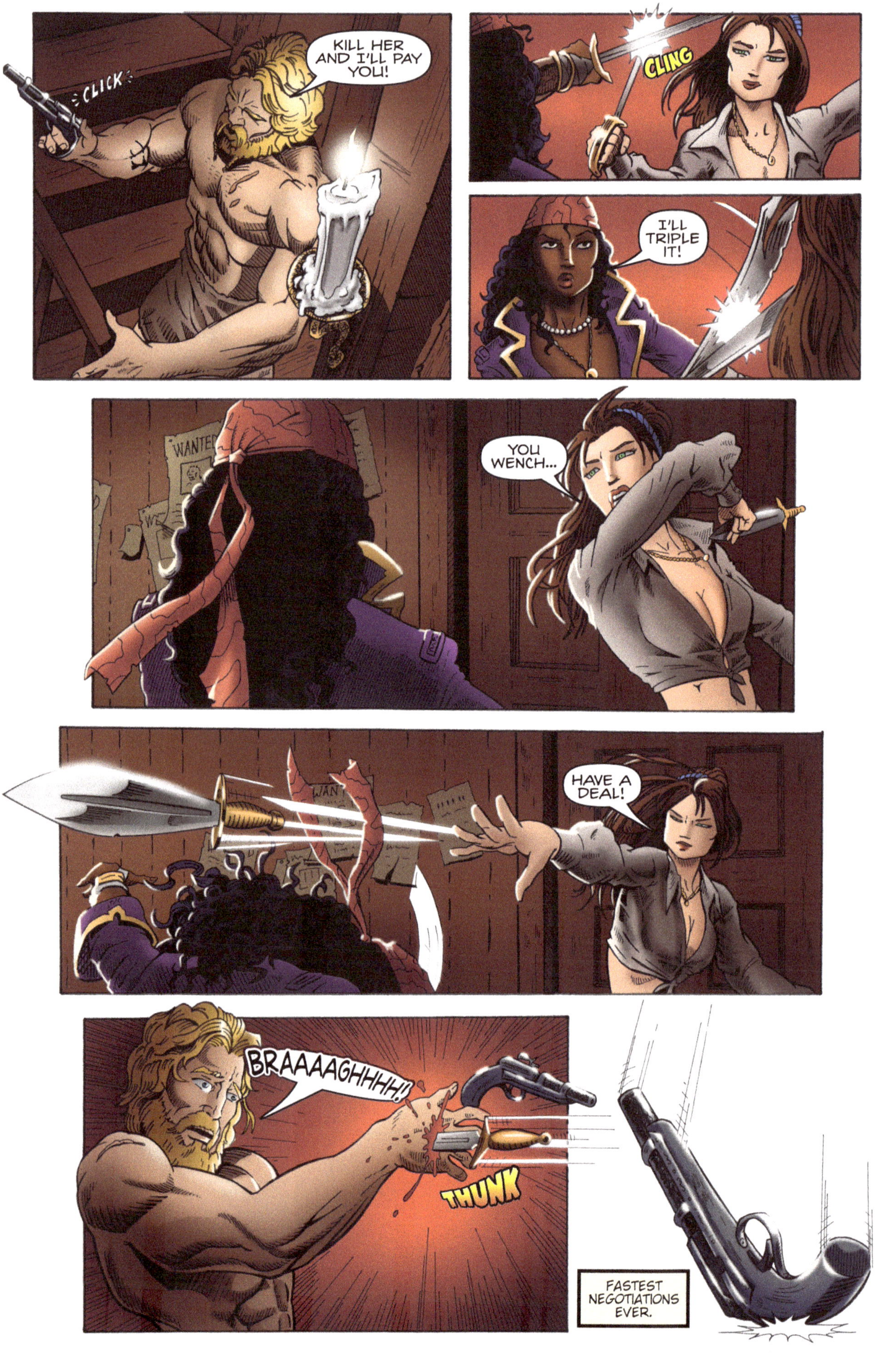
CLICK
KILL HER AND I'LL PAY YOU!
CLING
I'LL TRIPLE IT!
WANTED
YOU WENCH...
HAVE A DEAL!
BRAAAAGHHHH!
THUNK
FASTEST NEGOTIATIONS EVER.

"YEAH, THAT CAPTAIN WAS HOT, BUT HIS CANNON MISFIRES."

"EWW."

"TELL ME MORE ABOUT ZIS TREASURE."

"MY FATHER WAS A SEA SNAKE, BUT HIS LEGACY IS UNDENIABLE."

"HE LOGGED HIS ENTIRE LIFE IN ONE BOOK."

"THE TREASURES, MAPS, SAILING ROUTES, AND THE PEOPLE HE CAME TO KNOW."

"AND IT JUST SO HAPPENS I JUST STOLE THAT BOOK FROM A NAKED MAN."

VENGEANCE
STEP 1 ON OUR EPIC ADVENTURE IS TO STEAL MY BOAT.
STEAL *YOUR* BOAT?!
IT'S MY FAVORITE GAME TO PLAY WITH A GIRLFRIEND; DAMSEL IN DISTRESS. THE SUCCESS RATE IS 98%.

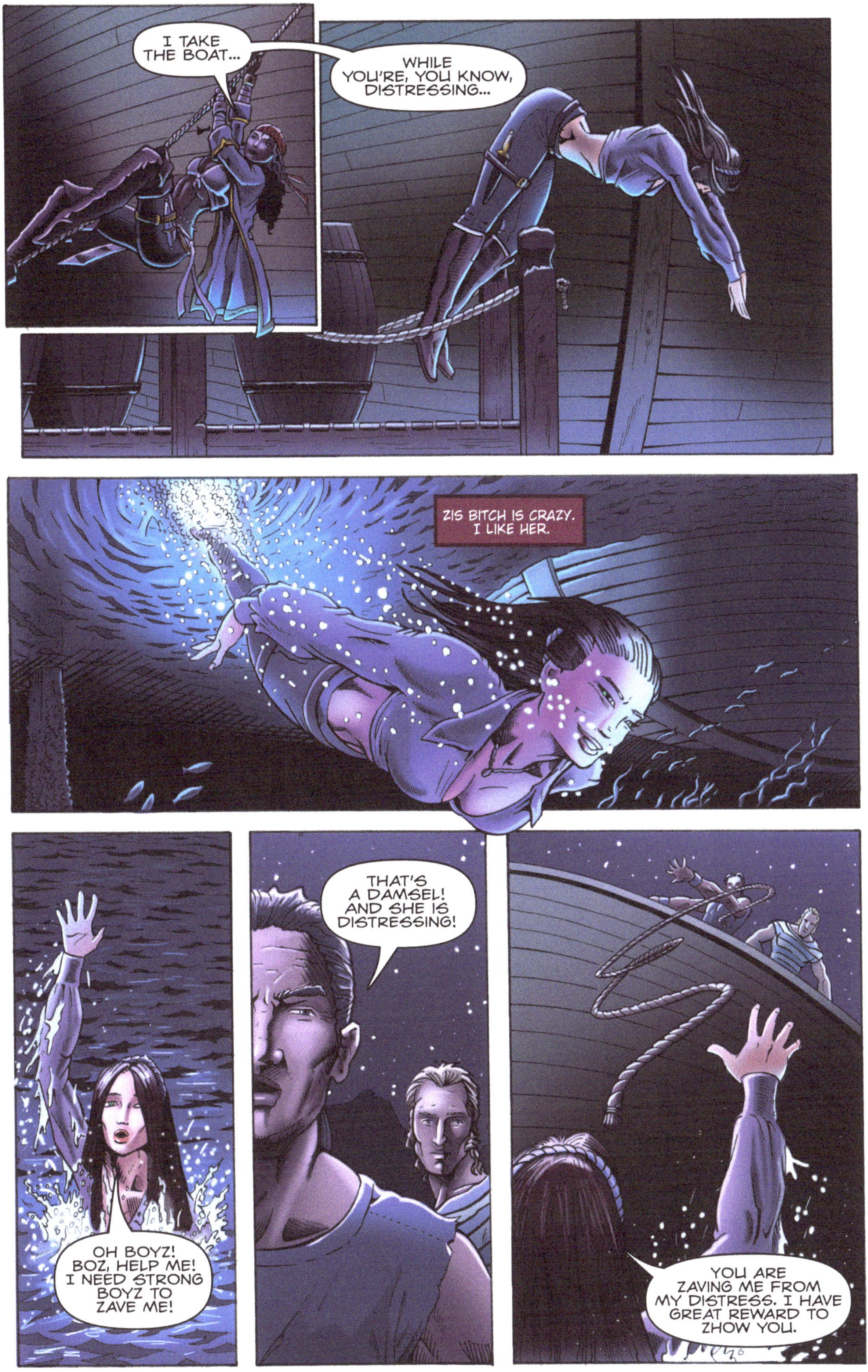
I TAKE THE BOAT...
WHILE YOU'RE, YOU KNOW, DISTRESSING...
ZIS BITCH IS CRAZY. I LIKE HER.
OH BOYZ! BOZ, HELP ME! I NEED STRONG BOYZ TO ZAVE ME!
THAT'S A DAMSEL! AND SHE IS DISTRESSING!
YOU ARE ZAVING ME FROM MY DISTRESS. I HAVE GREAT REWARD TO ZHOW YOU.

WER' HAPPY TA HELP LASSIE.
WE NEED TA' GIT THESE COLD WET CLOSE OFF YA' NOW.
CLICK
98%. I AM IMPREZZED.
IT IS INEVITABLE. MEN THINK WITH THEIR PISTOLS FIRST.

WE'RE COMMANDEERING THIS SHIP. YOUR CAPTAIN IS DEAD AND WE'RE HEADIN' TOWARD THE WORLD'S MOST INCREDIBLE BOOTY.

JOIN OUR CREW OR JUMP OVA'BOARD.

DID YOU SAY BOOTY?

YES, BOOTY. SO MUCH BOOTY.

I HATE TO BRAG BUT DAT WAS ONE HELL-OF-A NIGHT. BOOK, CREW, BOAT. IF ONLY MY DAD COULD SEE ME NOW.
MUTINY. MUTINY CAPTAIN. HALF YA' CREW WAS JUST THROWN OVA' BOARD.
NO! NO ONE HAS SHANKED ME SO, SINCE CAPTAIN BLACKBEARD HIMSELF.
THAT WAZ HIS DAUGHTER.
YOUR FAMILY SUCKS!

I UNDERSTAND WE'RE OFF TO A STRANGE START... CUTE HAT... BUT THE MOST REWARD COMES WITH THE MOST RISK.

WHO IS READY FOR SOME REWARD?!

16 YEARS EARLIER

I'LL NEVER FORGET THE FEAR IN MY MOTHER'S EYES.

KNOCK KNOCK KNOCK

QUIET AS A CHURCH MOUSE NOW, HANNAH.

DO NOT OPEN THIS DOOR.

A MESSAGE FOR YOUR HUSBAND.

THUMP

I WAS 6 YEARS OLD. I NEVER CHOSE MY FATHER'S PIRATE LIFE...

IT CHOSE ME.

VERY FEW 6 YEAR OLDS UNDERSTAND REVENGE. BUT I DID... AND I WANTED IT.

"JUST A MESSENGER, MA'AM."

"REMEMBER WHEN WE PLAYED ANIMALS? I NEED YOU TO BECOME A MOUSE..."

I WAS IN THE CLOSET FOR HOURS...

BEFORE I COULD SUMMON UP THE COURAGE TO OPEN THE DOOR.

ALL THESE YEARS LATER, I STILL WAKE UP AT NIGHT AND THINK I'M BACK HIDING IN THE DARK...

THE THOUGHT OF 'COULD I HAVE DONE SOMETHING TO SAVE MY MOTHER' PULLS ME DOWN LIKE AN ANCHOR TO THE SEA FLOOR.
CAPTAIN, WE HAVE A SQUALL ON ZE FORWARD ZIDE.
ALL CREW ON DECK.
THEY SAY, 'BEFORE YOU EMBARK ON A JOURNEY OF REVENGE, DIG TWO GRAVES.'
I'LL GLADLY LAY IN MINE, AS LONG AS MY MOTHER'S MURDERER IS IN THE DIRT NEXT TO ME.

ALL CREW READY.
WE'RE MIZZING ONE.
BELOW DECK ZLEEPING NO DOUBT.
MOST LIKELY RAIDING IN DE' CUPBOARDS FOR POTATOES.
OR DOING WHATEVER IS IT IS THE GROSS MEN BE DOING.
DIDN'T ZEE ZIZ ONE COMING.

Panel 1: OH, I'M SORRY... I UM, WAS JUST GONNA...

Panel 2: A SHIP IS NO PLACE FOR ZECRETS YOUNG LADY.

Panel 3: I HAD TO GET AWAY FROM MY VIOLENT BOYFRIEND YOU SEE, I...

I CARE ZERO.

Panel 4: PLEASE DON'T TELL THE CAPTAIN.

GET 'ER TIED DOWN. DUE NORTH. THIS BOAT WAS BUILT FOR STORMS!
WE PUSH STRAIGHT THROUGH! IF THIS WERE EASY, WEAKER MEN WOULD'VE TAKEN OUR PRIZE.
IT'S NO FUN IF YER LIFE ISN'T IN DANGER!

CAPTAIN, WE MUST SPEAK NOW. A CREWMAN WAZ...
UNHAND YER CAPTAIN!
PISHHT
FOCUS! WE'RE ABOUT TO FIGHT MOTHER NATURE...
AND SHE'S A RAGING BITCH. EVERYTHING ELSE CAN WAIT.

LISTEN UP CREW. WE ALL HAVE A PAST, SOME FULL OF REGRETS AND GHOSTS, BUT NONE A' THAT MATTERS RIGHT NOW. THIS IS THE PRESENT. EVERYTHING GOOD LIES AHEAD, JUST BEYOND THA' STORM.STAY CALM, STAY FOCUSED AND YOU'LL SEE THERE IS NOTHIN' WE CAN'T GET THROUGH TOGETHER! TO YER STATIONS!

MUCH LIES AHEAD; STORMS, ZOMBIES, AND SECRETS. NOTHING A SHARP SWORD AND VENGEANCE CAN'T HANDLE. EAT AN ORANGE TO FIGHT OFF SCURVY AND BATTEN DOWN THE HATCHES... IT'S GOING TO BE A ROUGH DAY AT SEA.

Bonus images

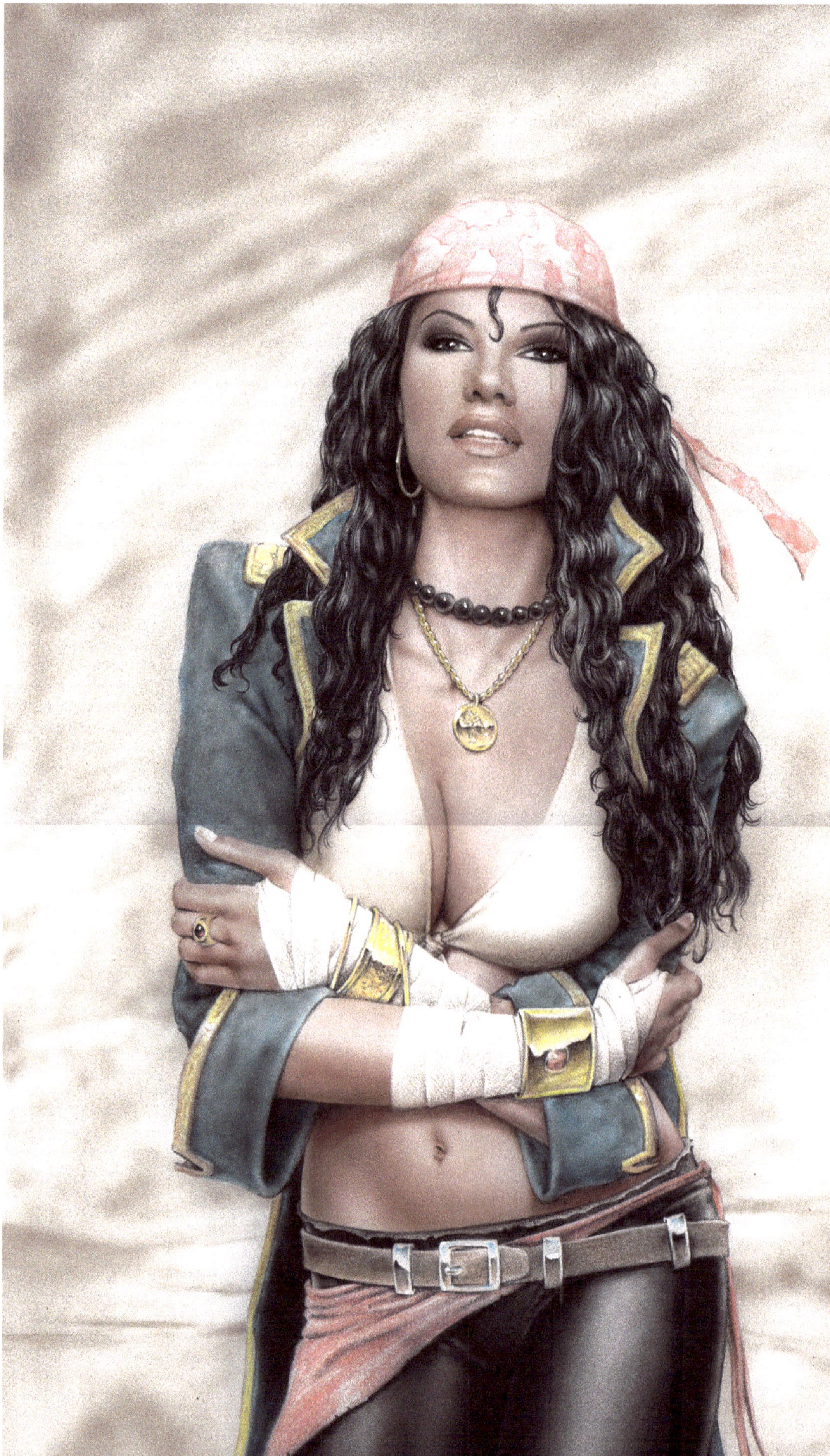

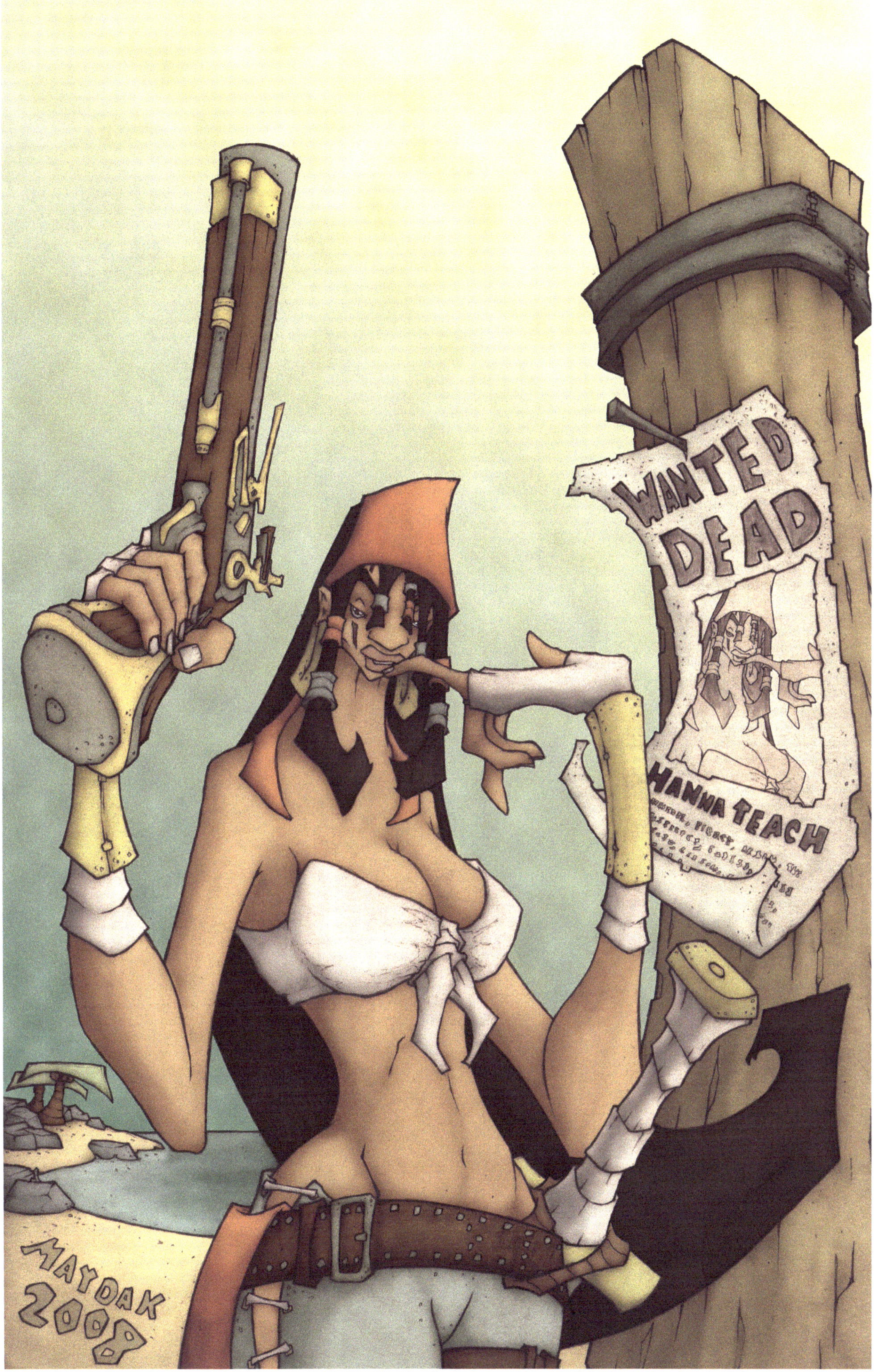
WANTED
DEAD
HANNA TEACH
MAYDAK
2008

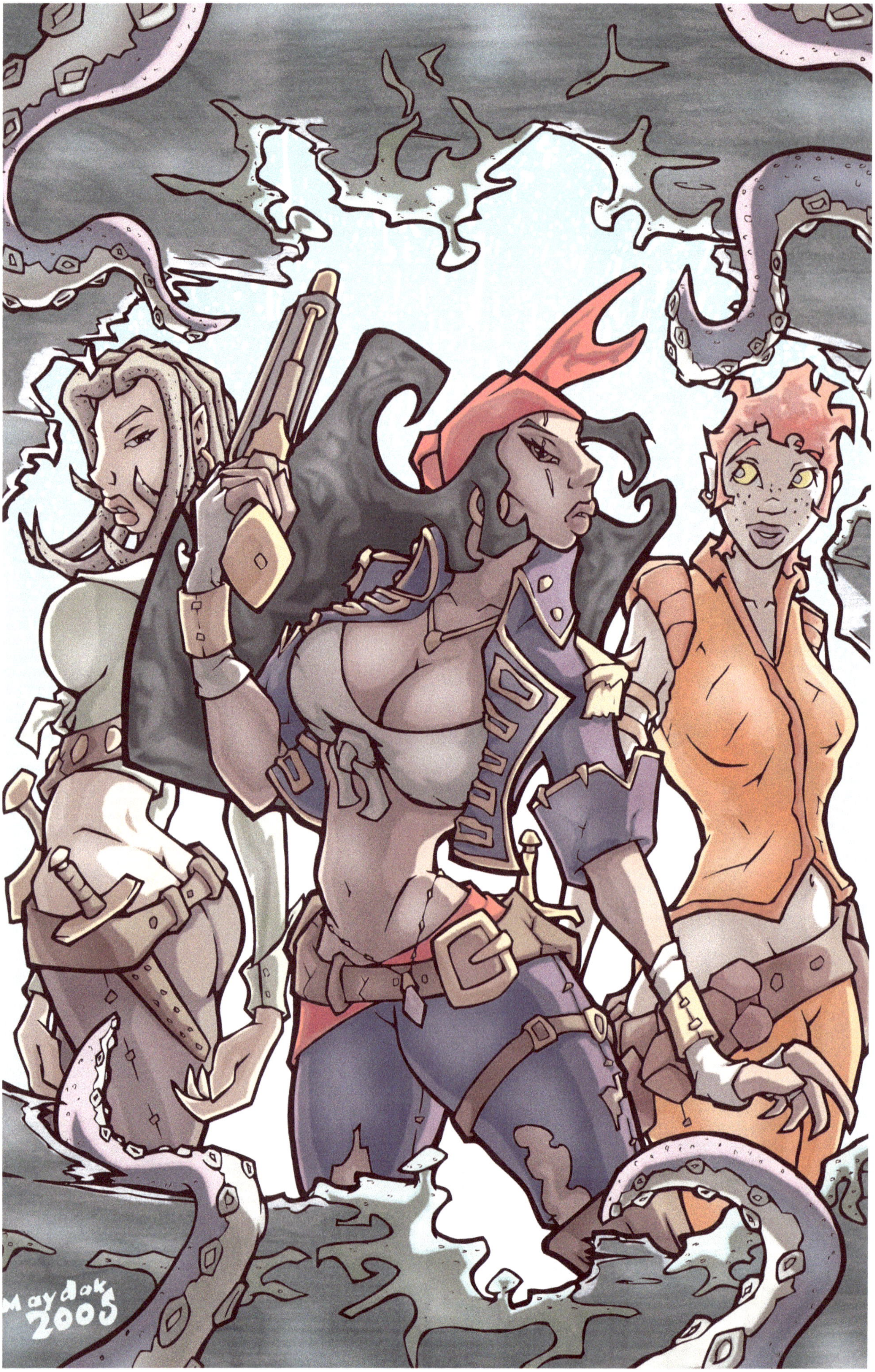
Maydak
2005

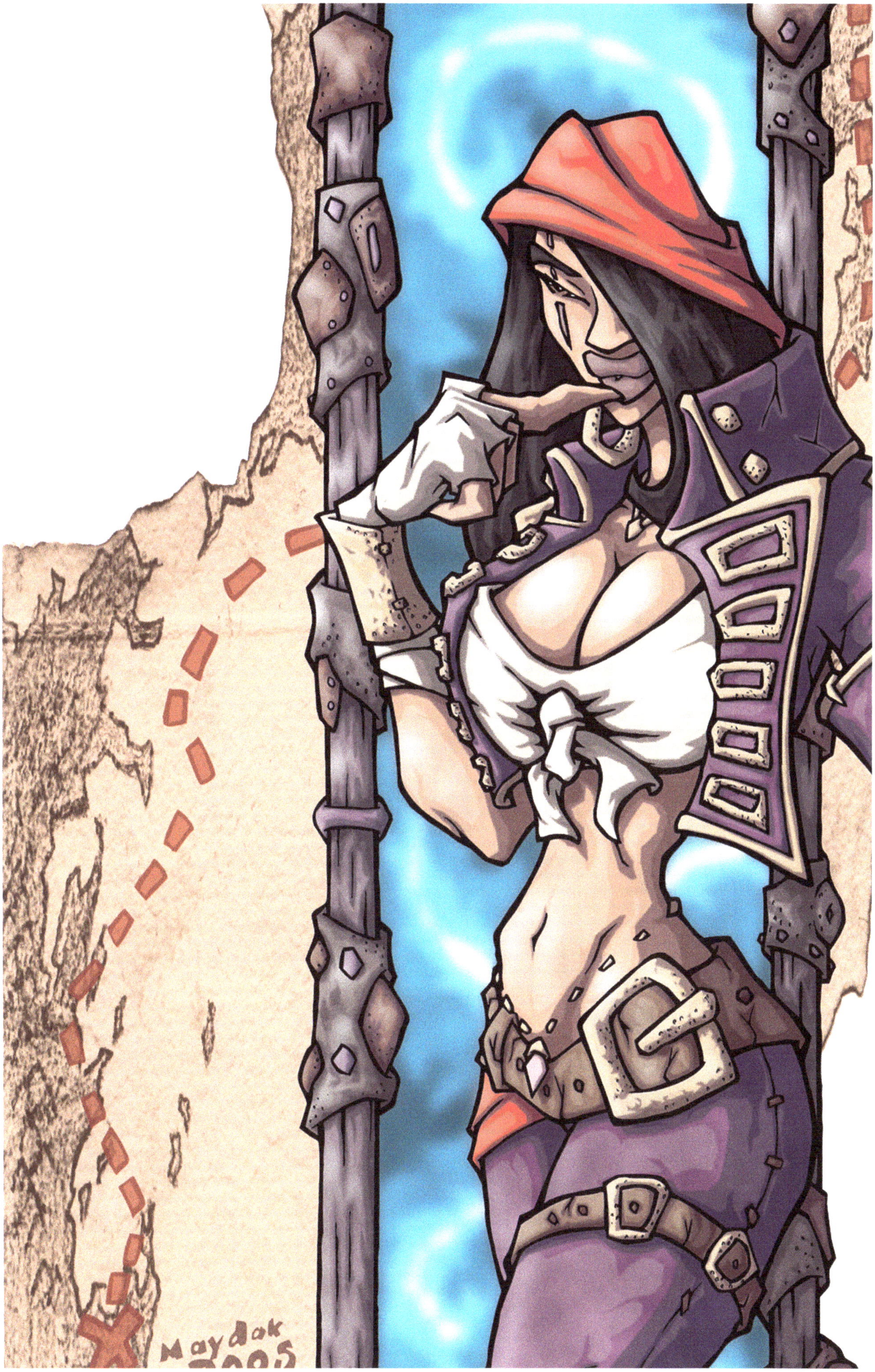
Maydak

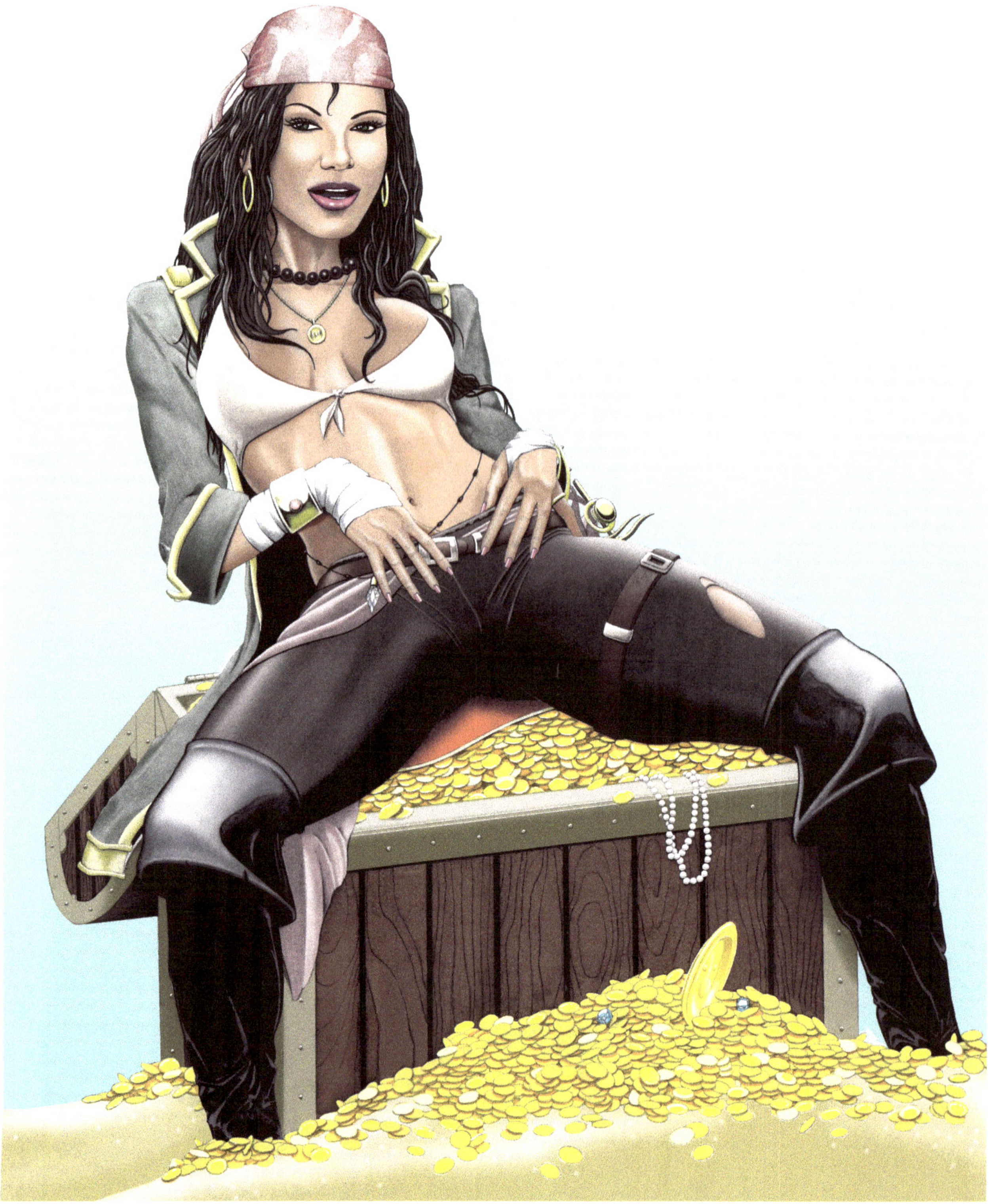

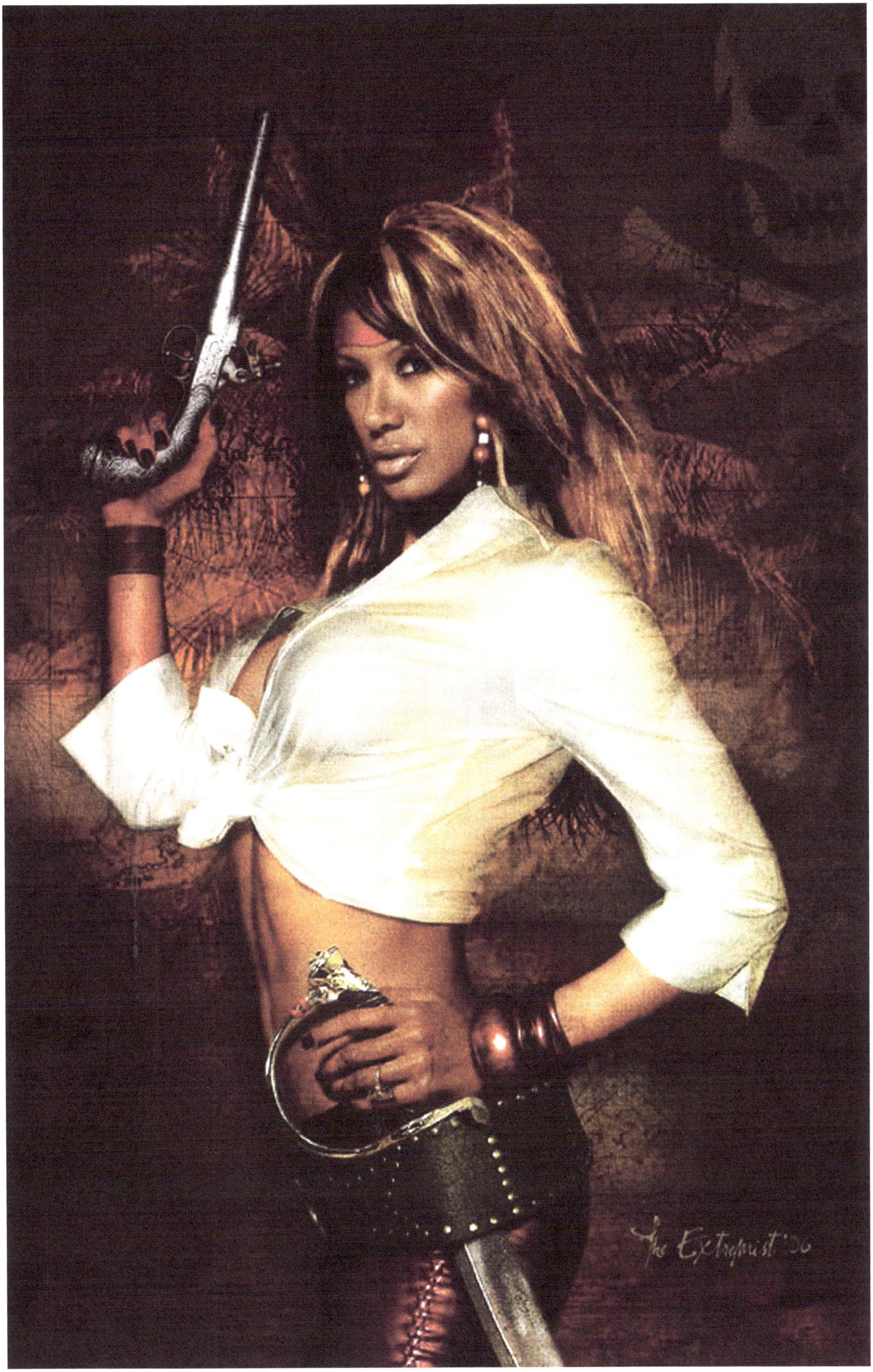

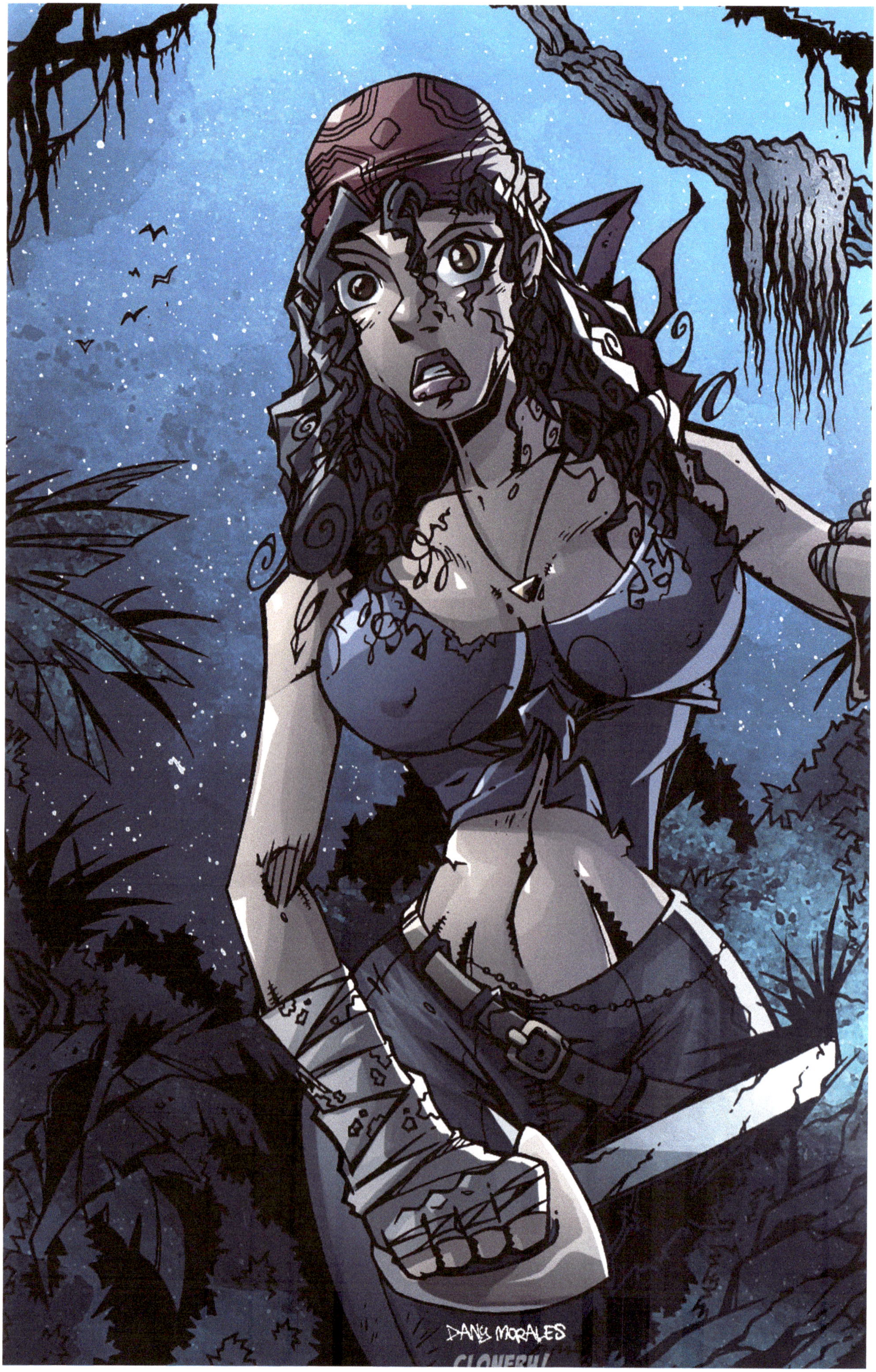
DANY MORALES

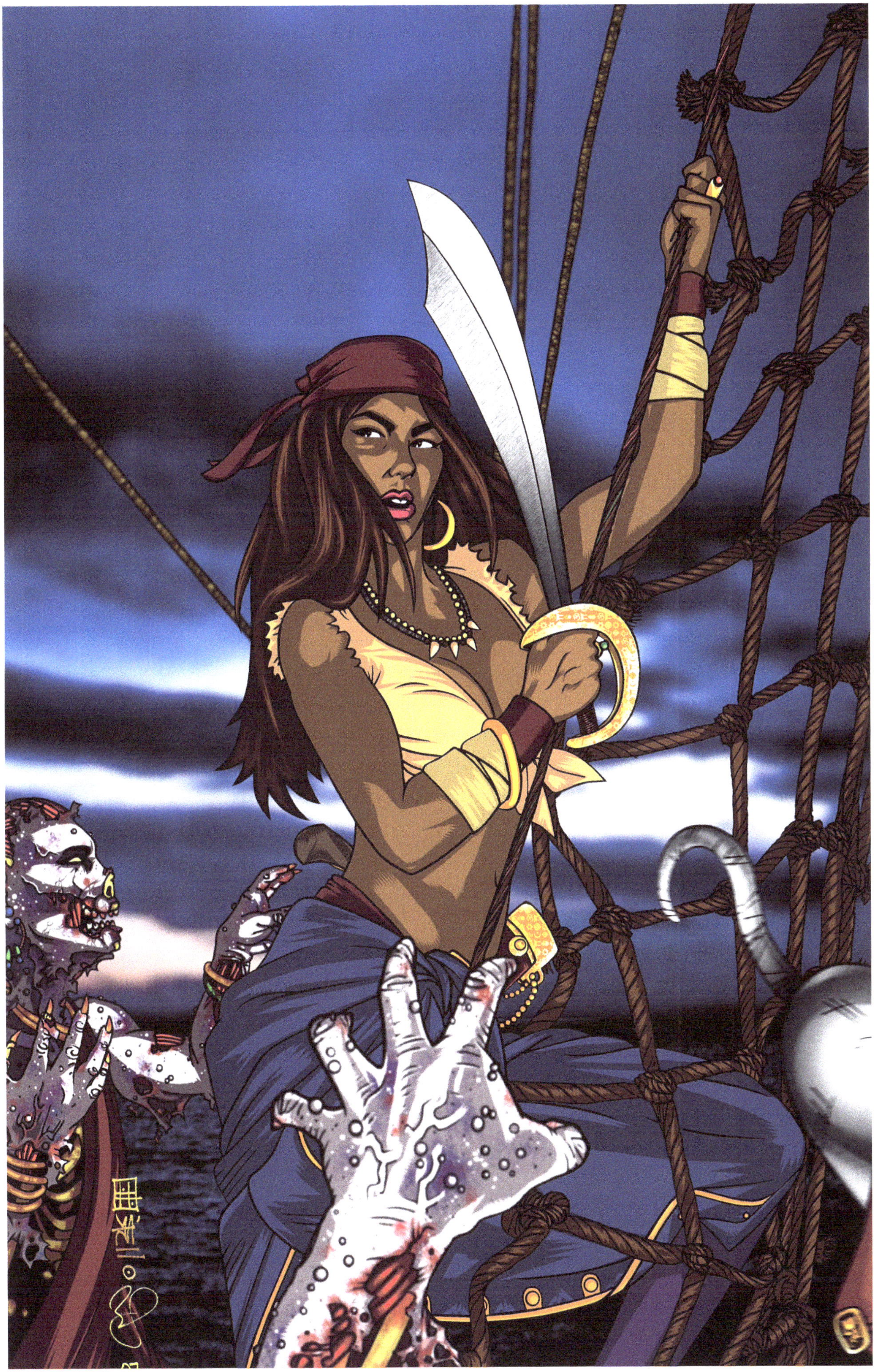

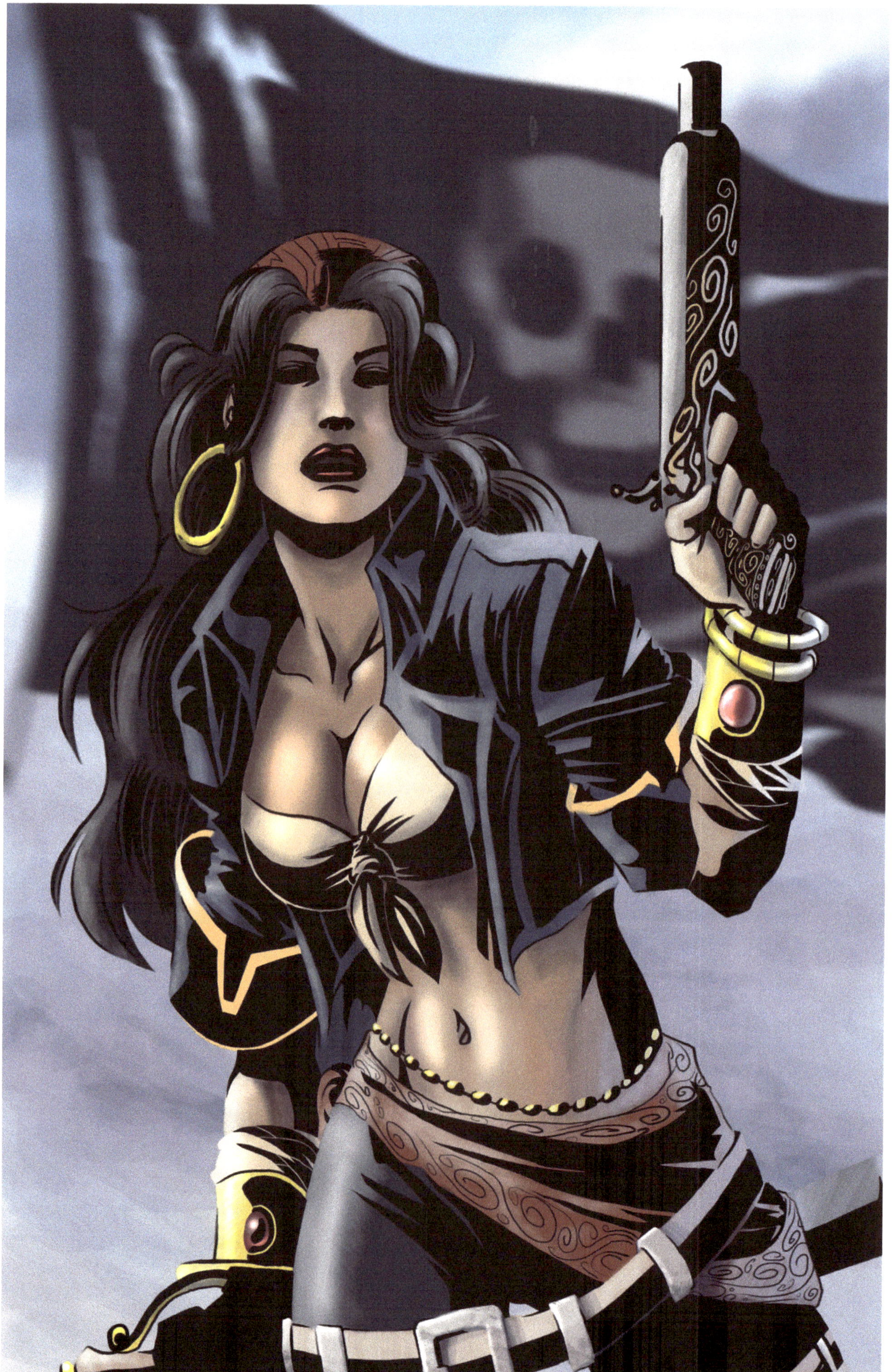

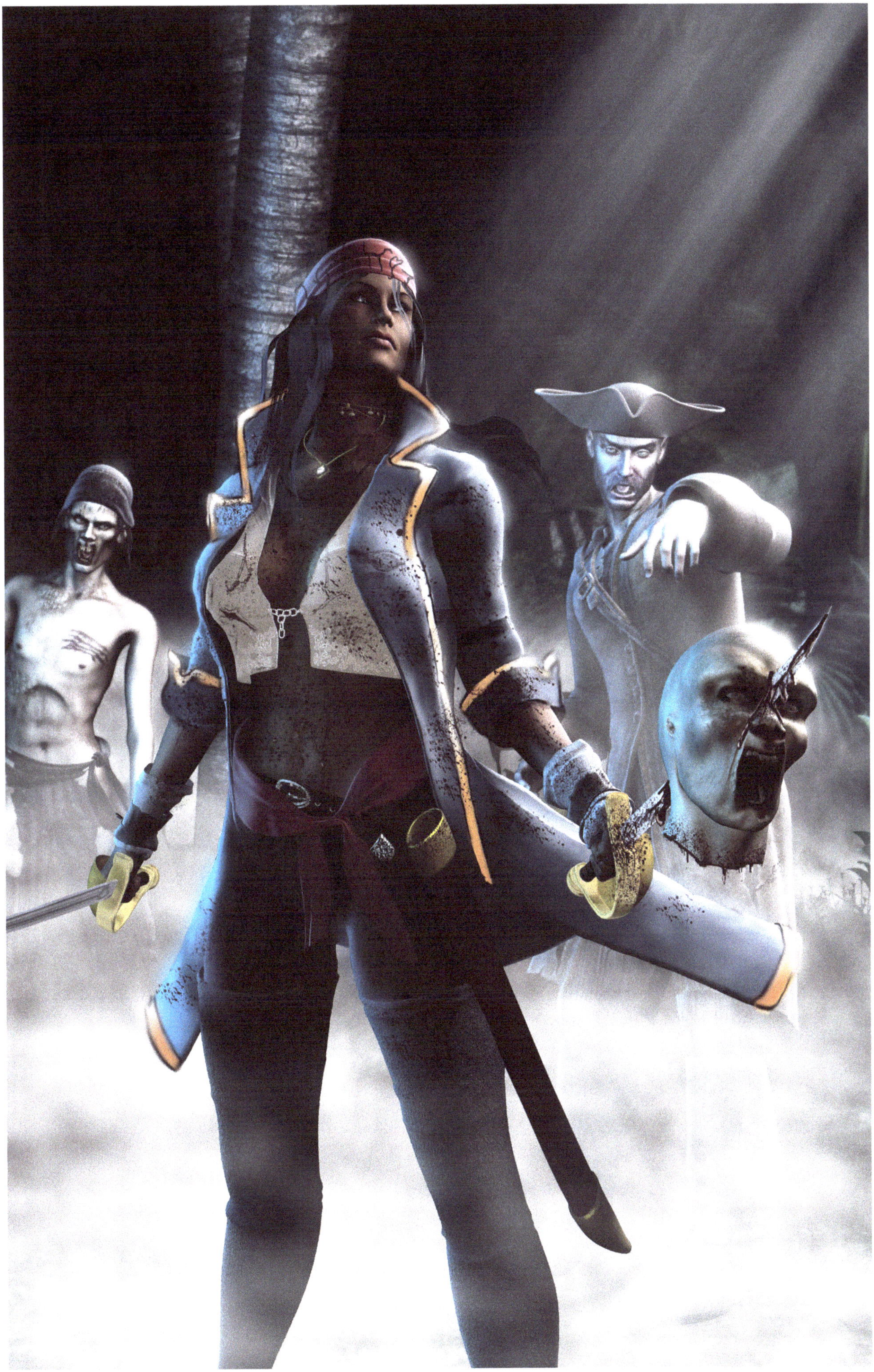

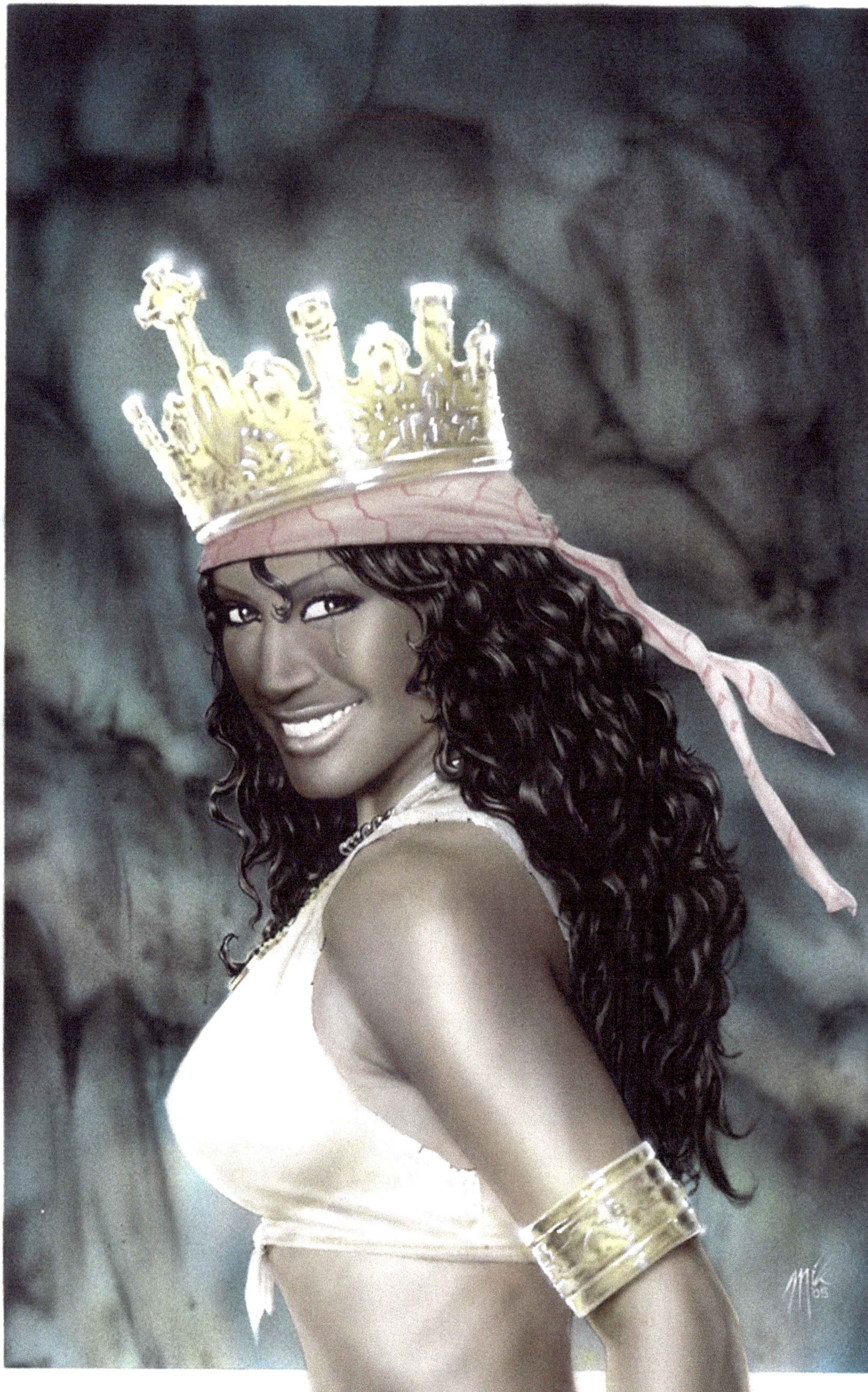

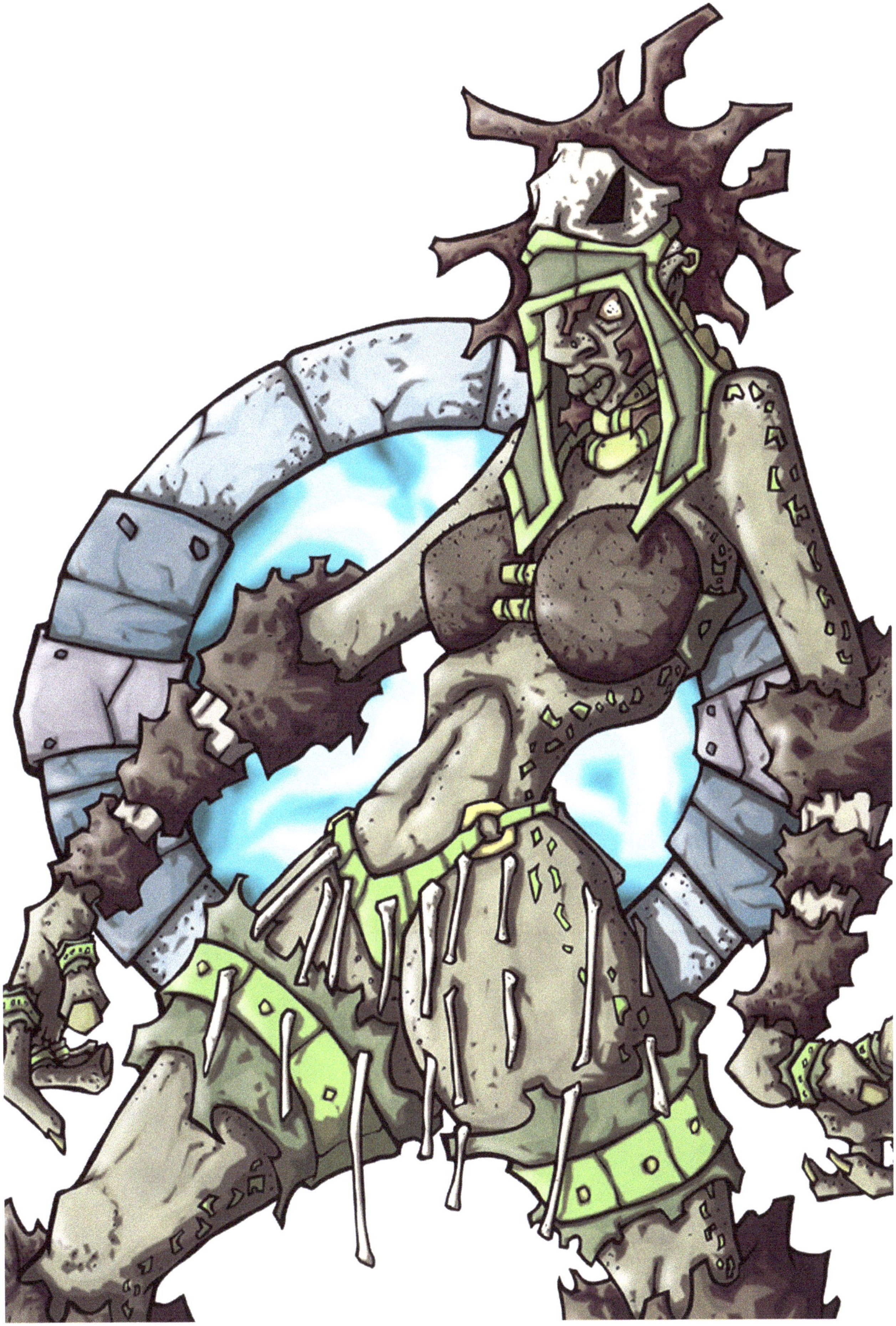

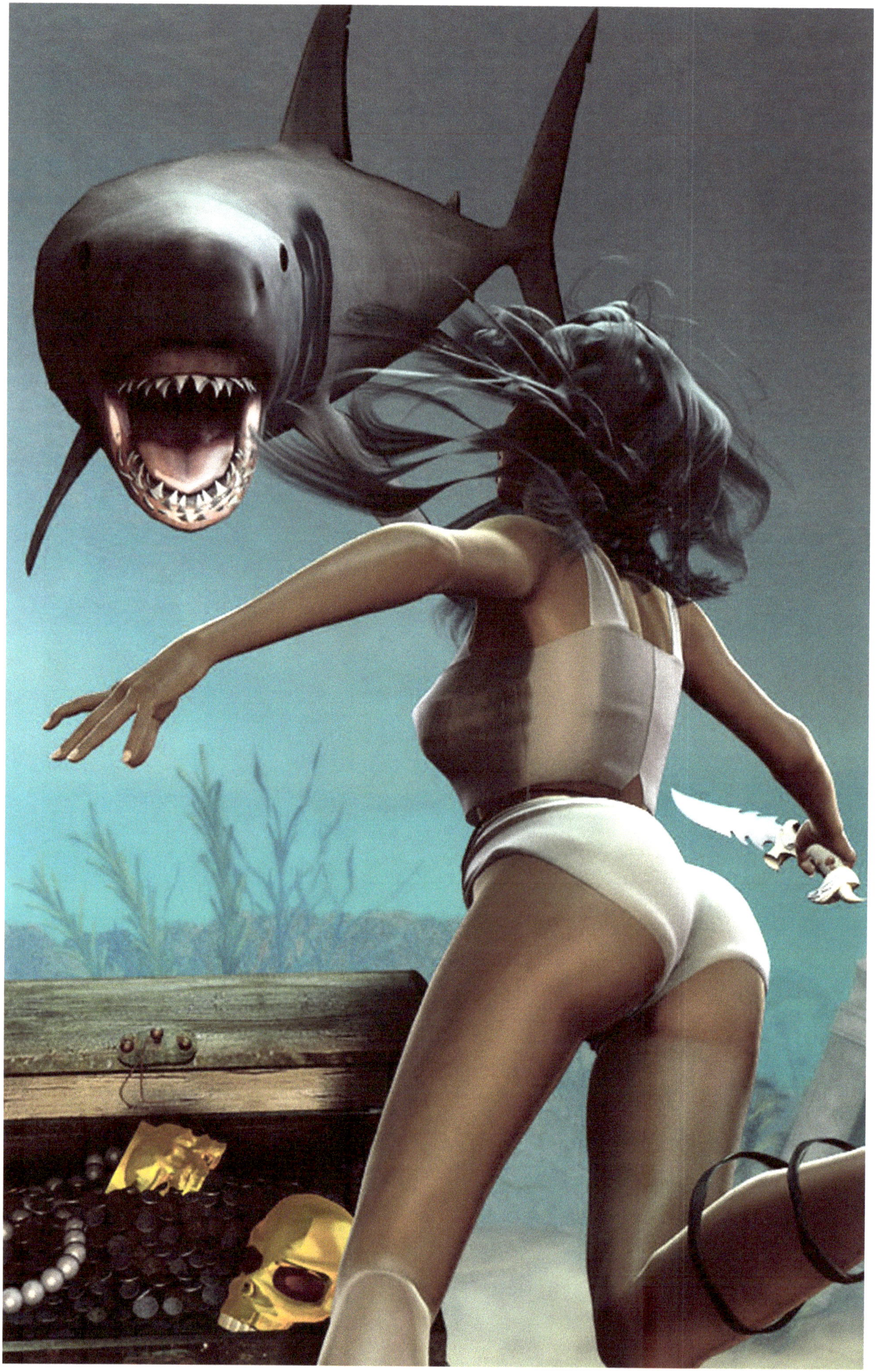

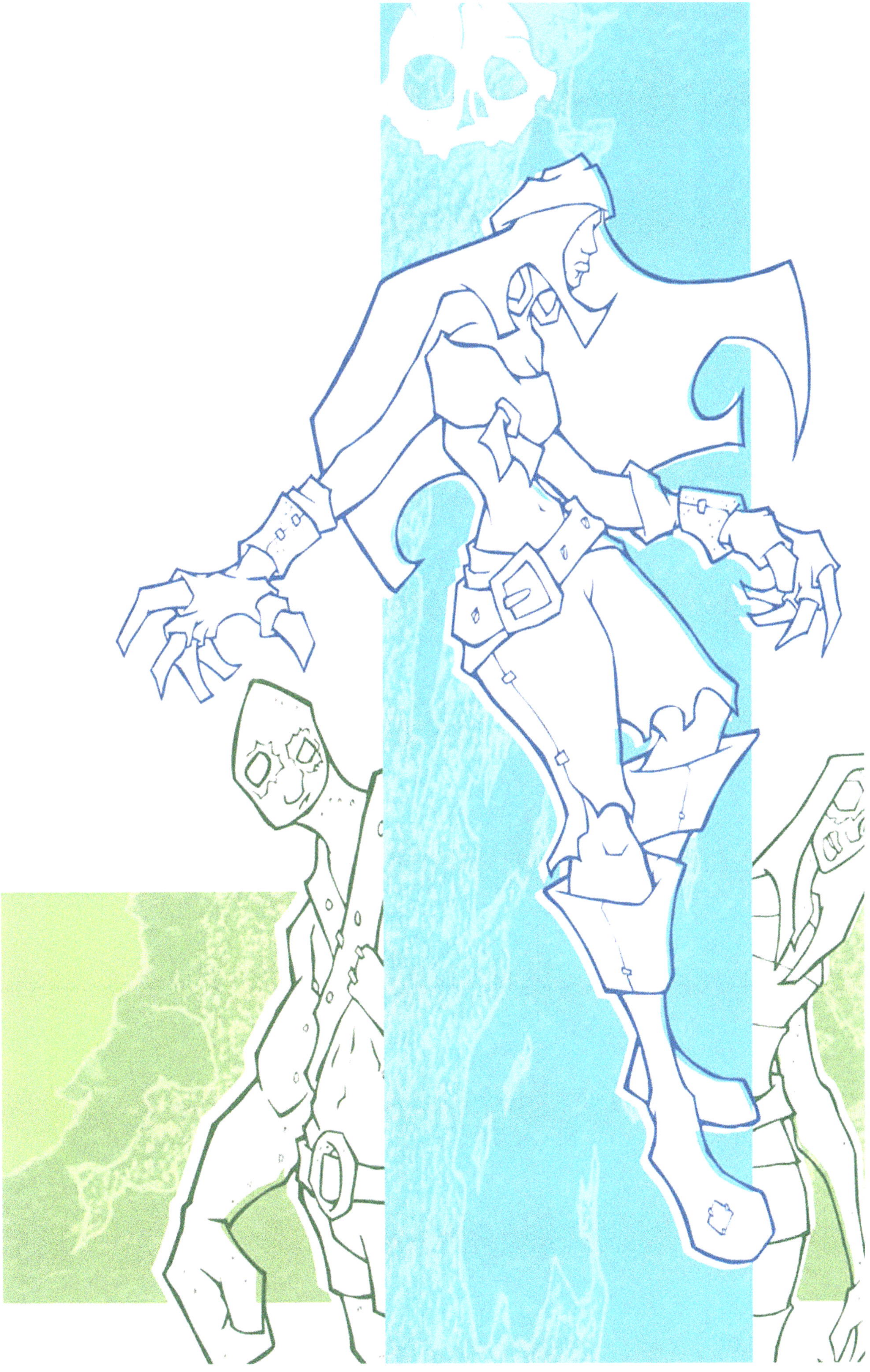

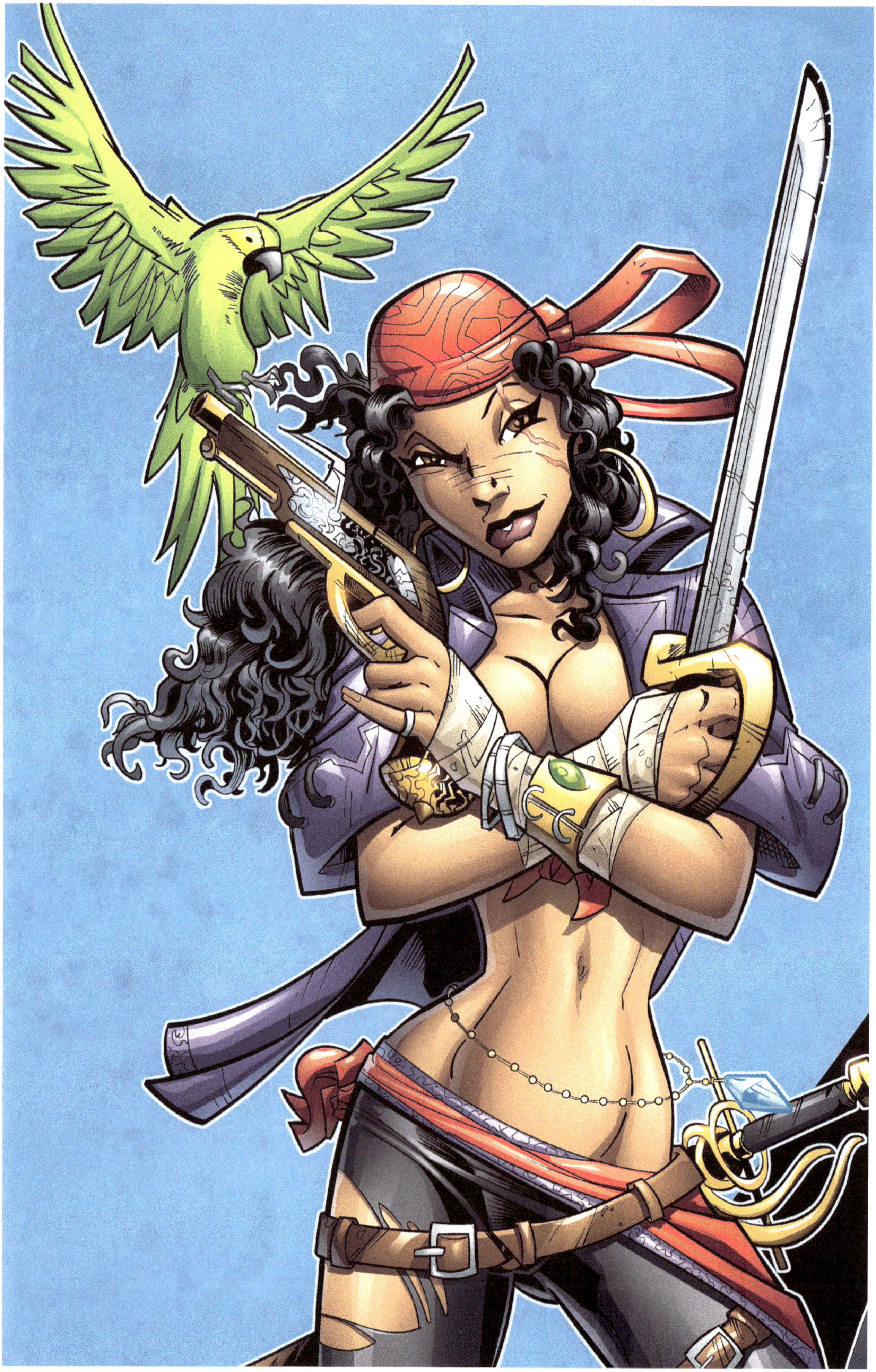

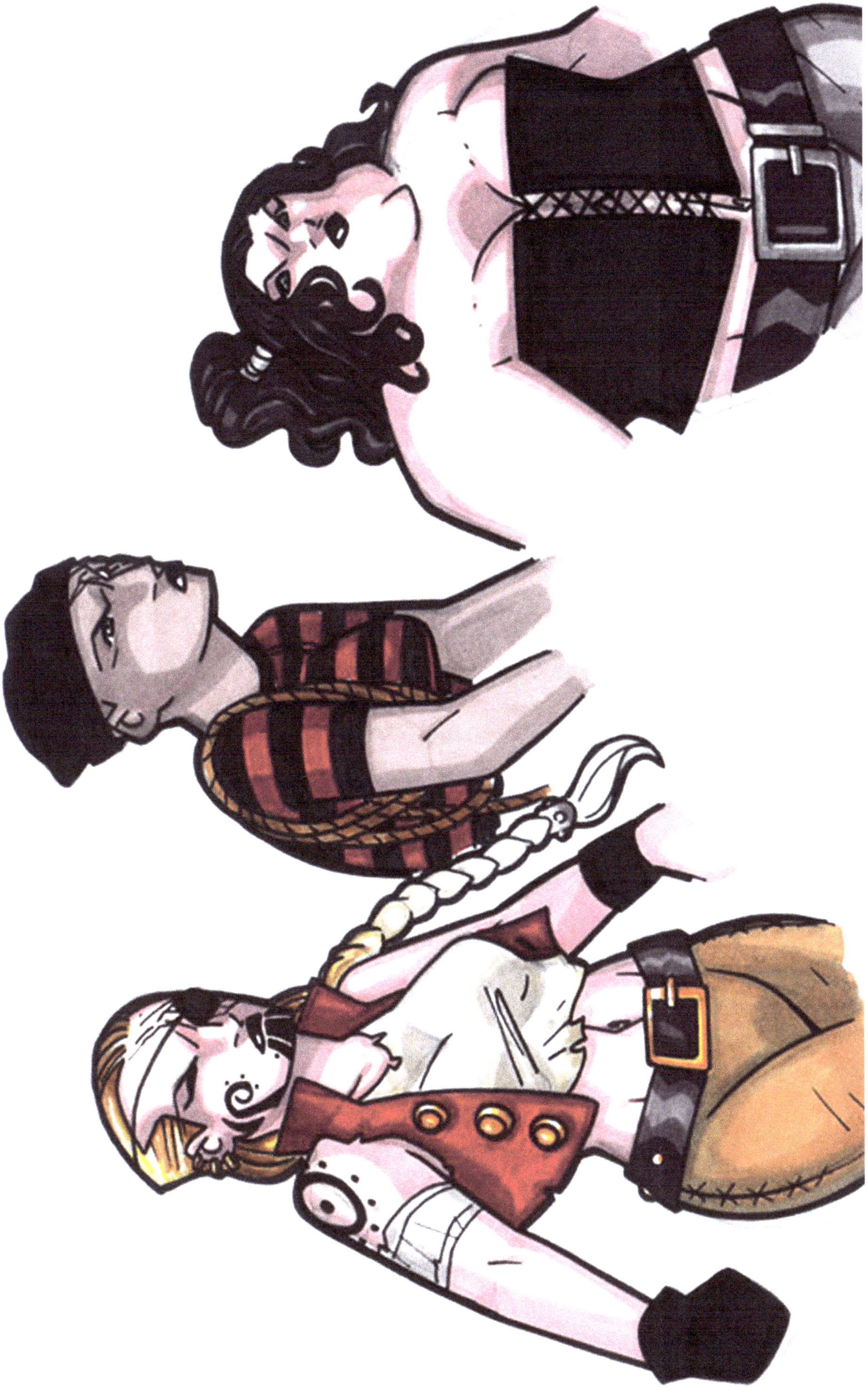

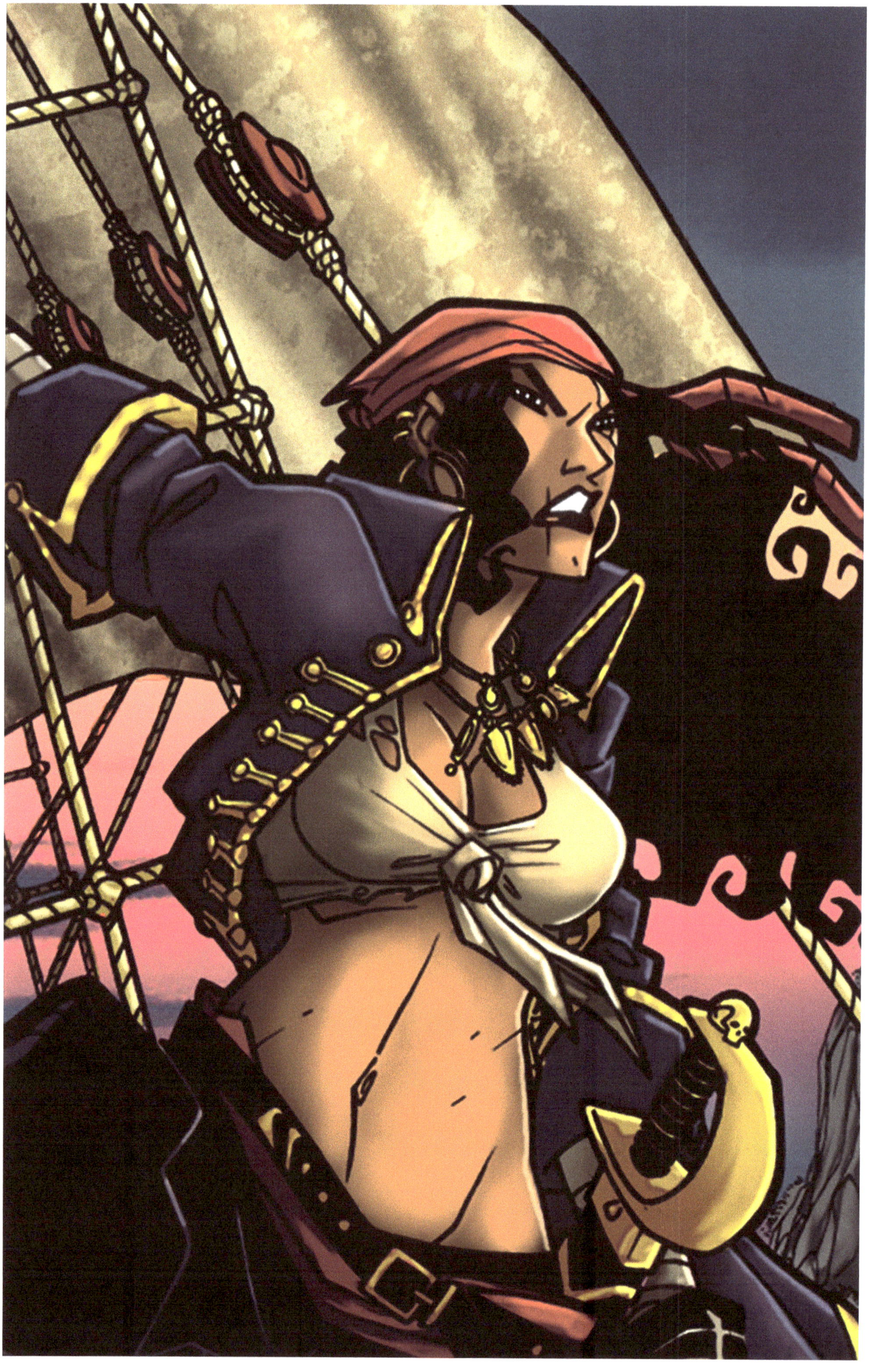

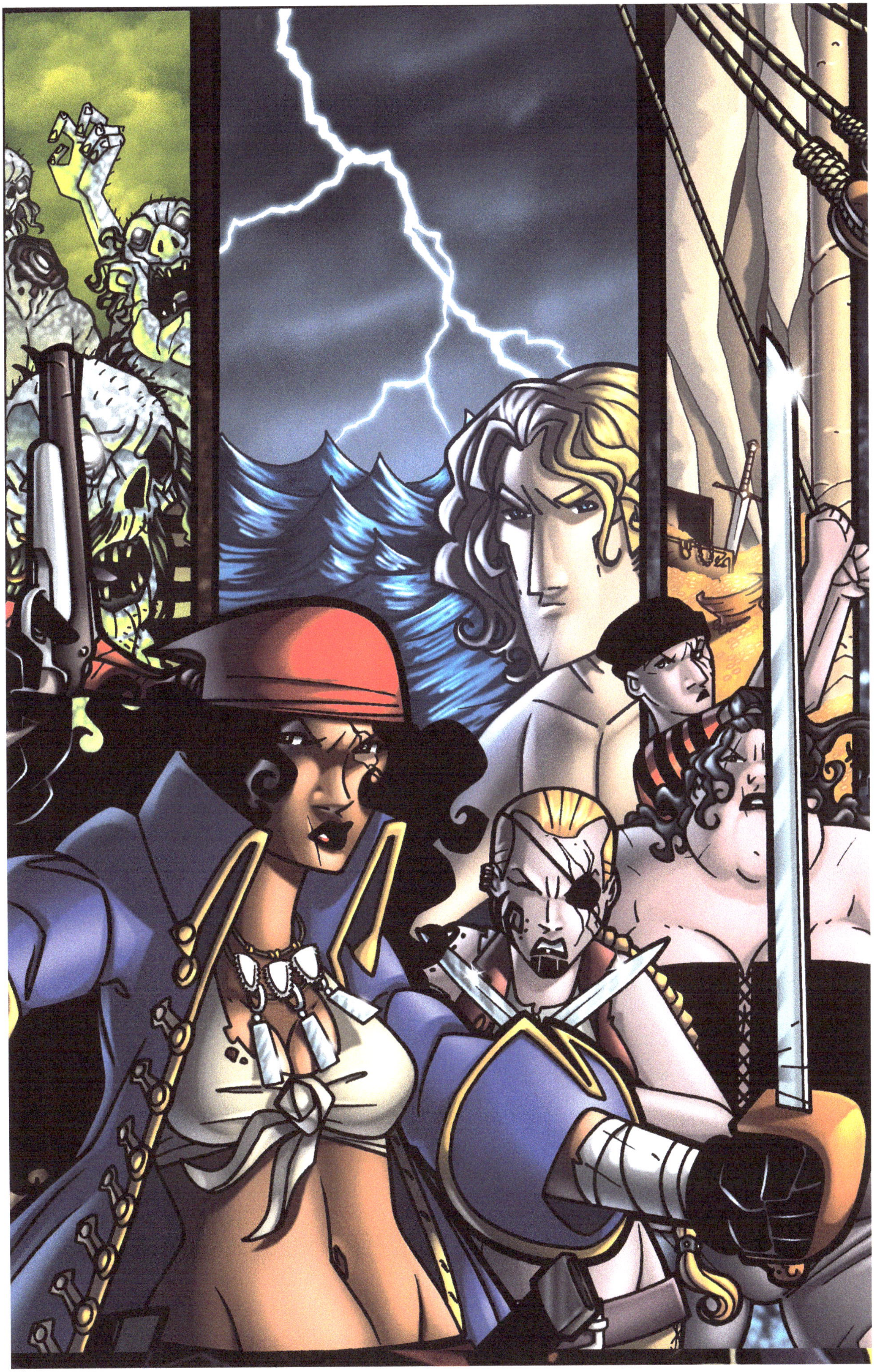

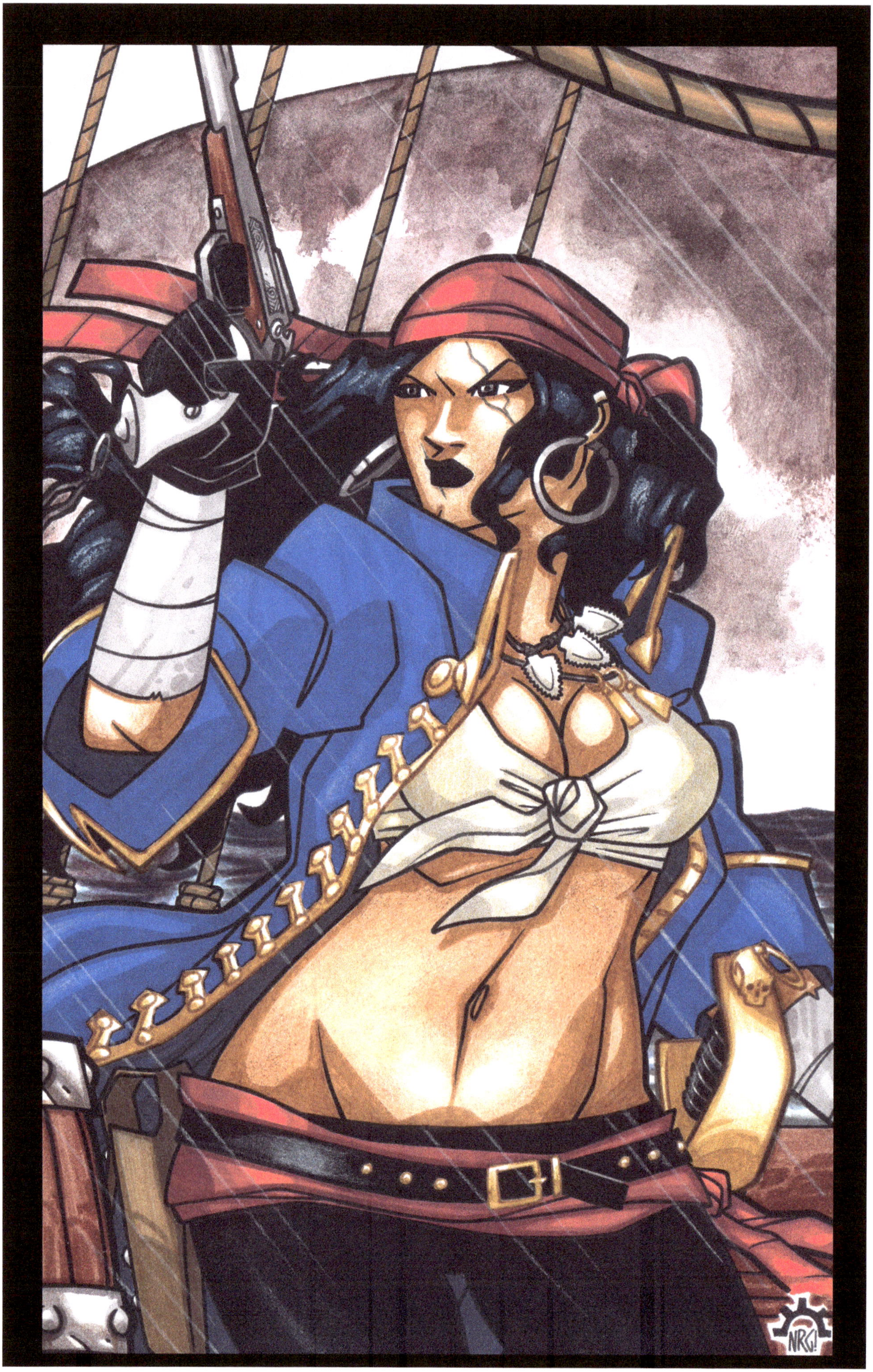

DAVID R. 2006

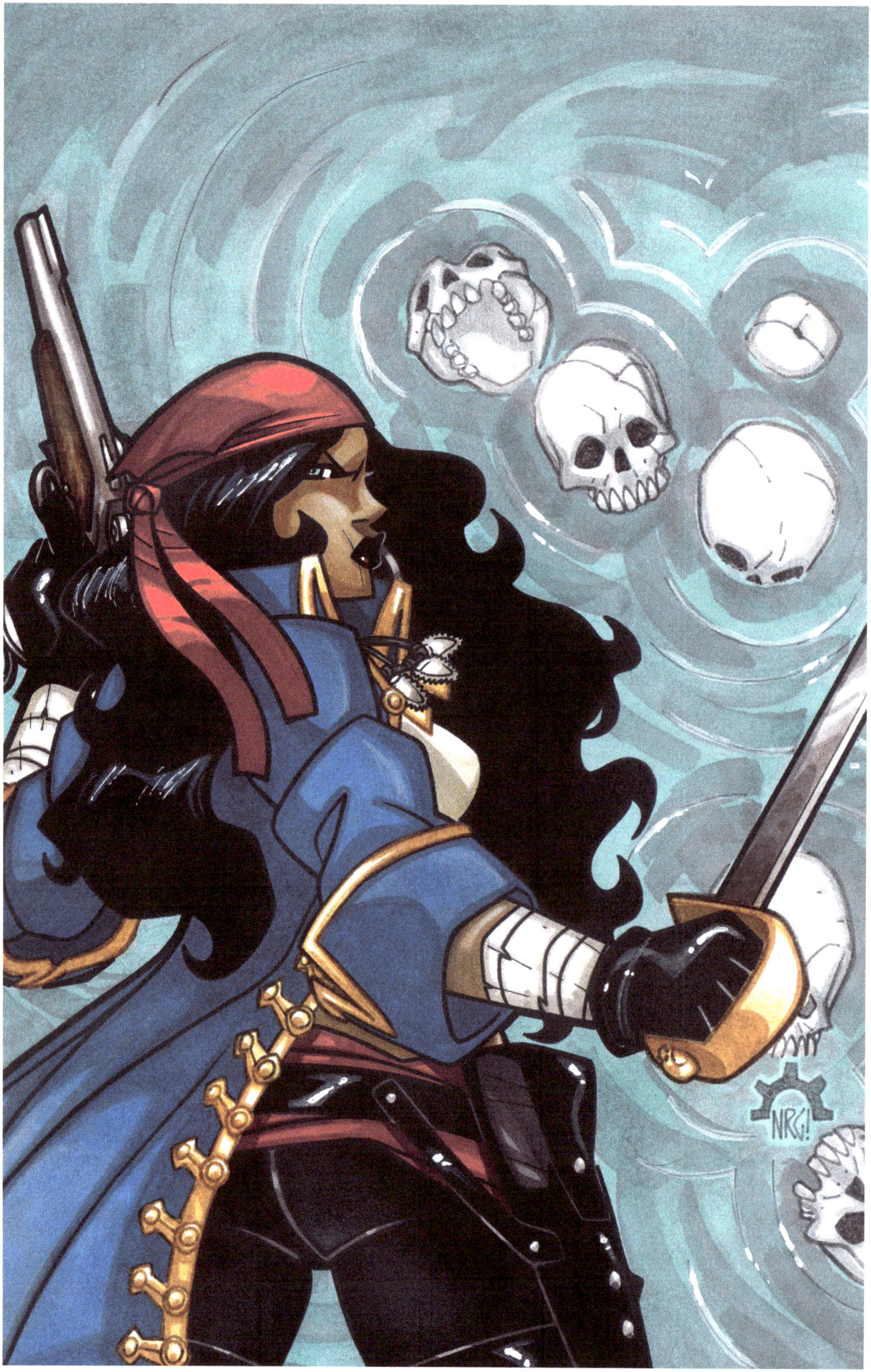

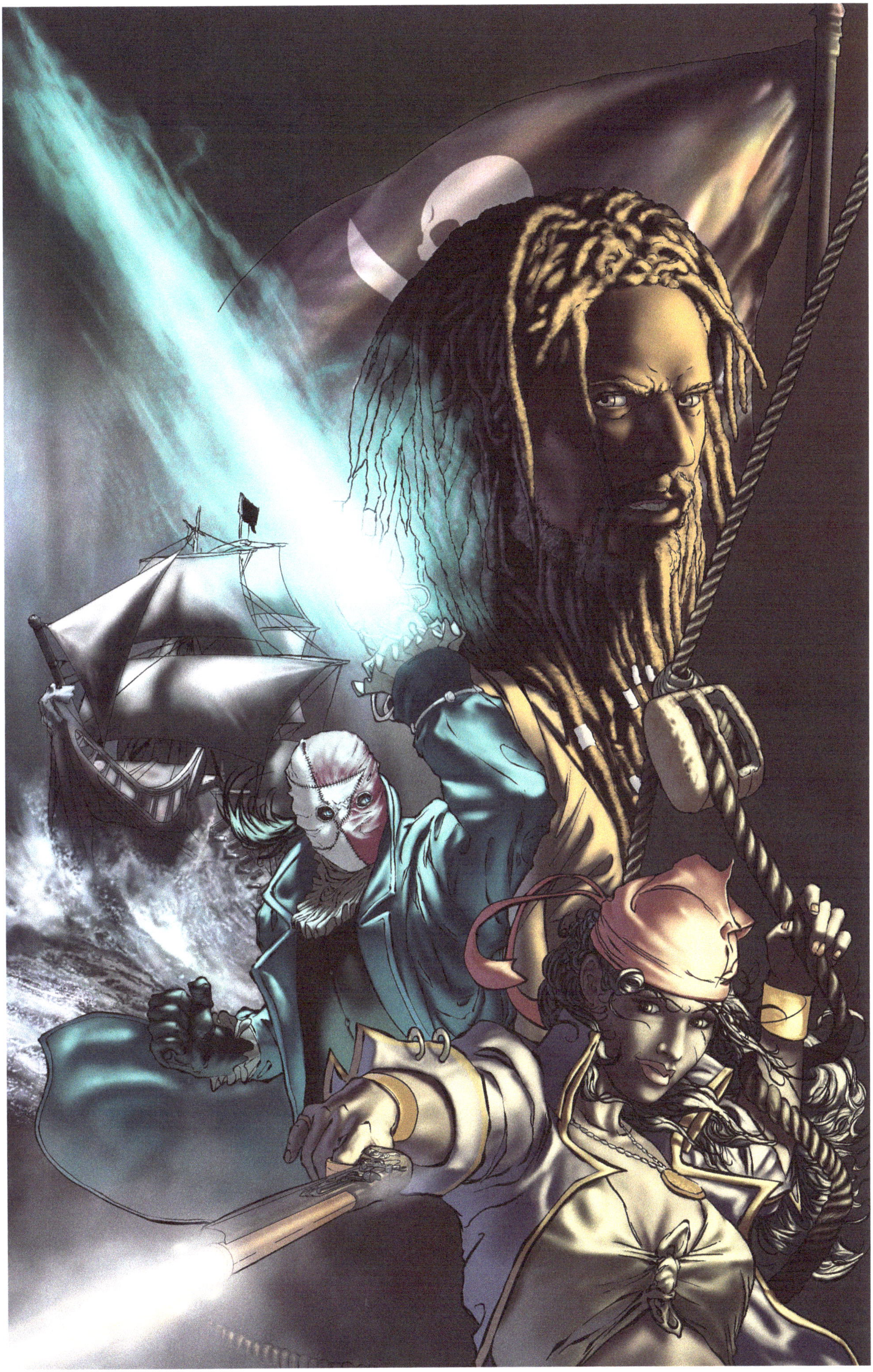

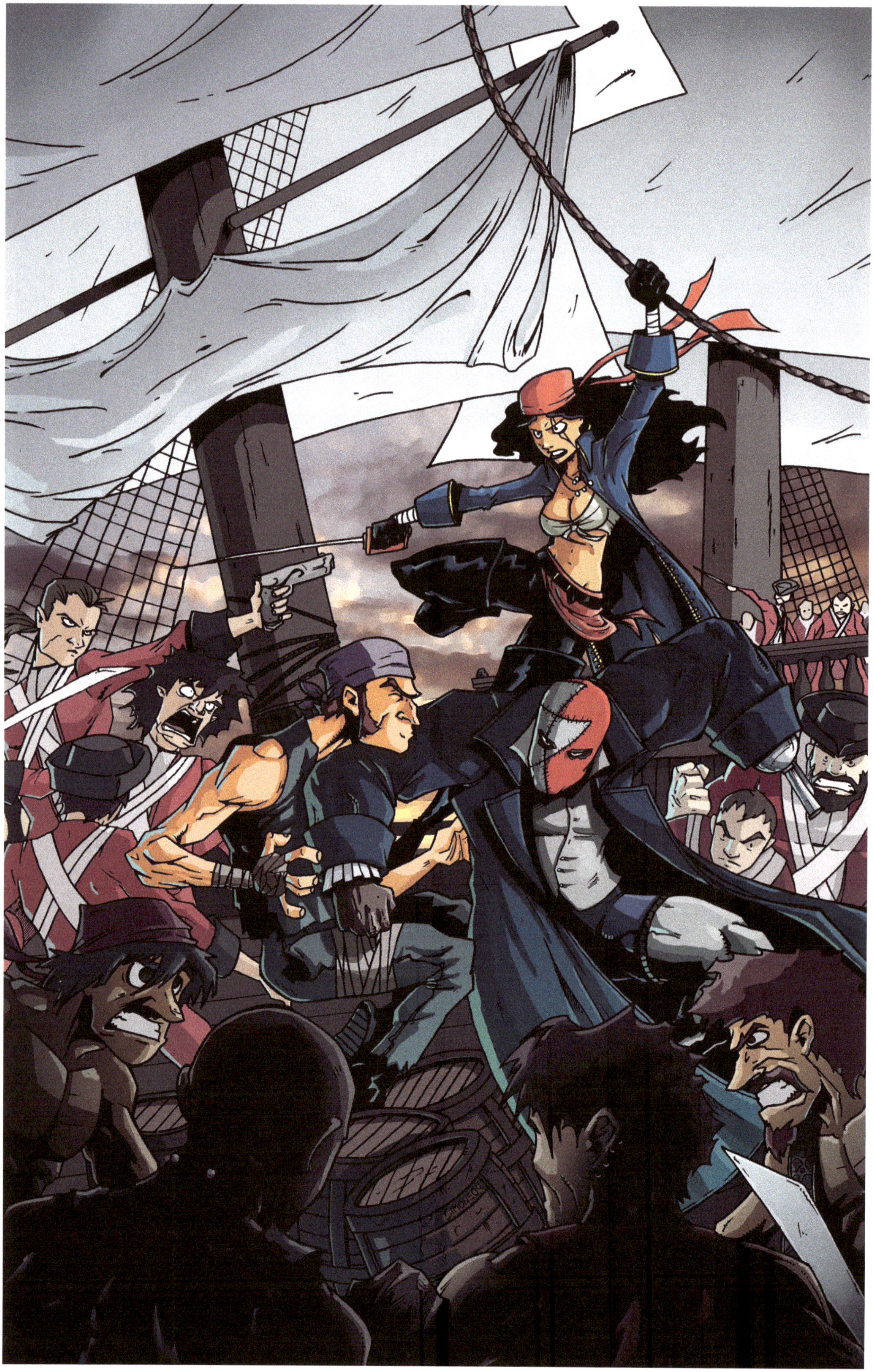

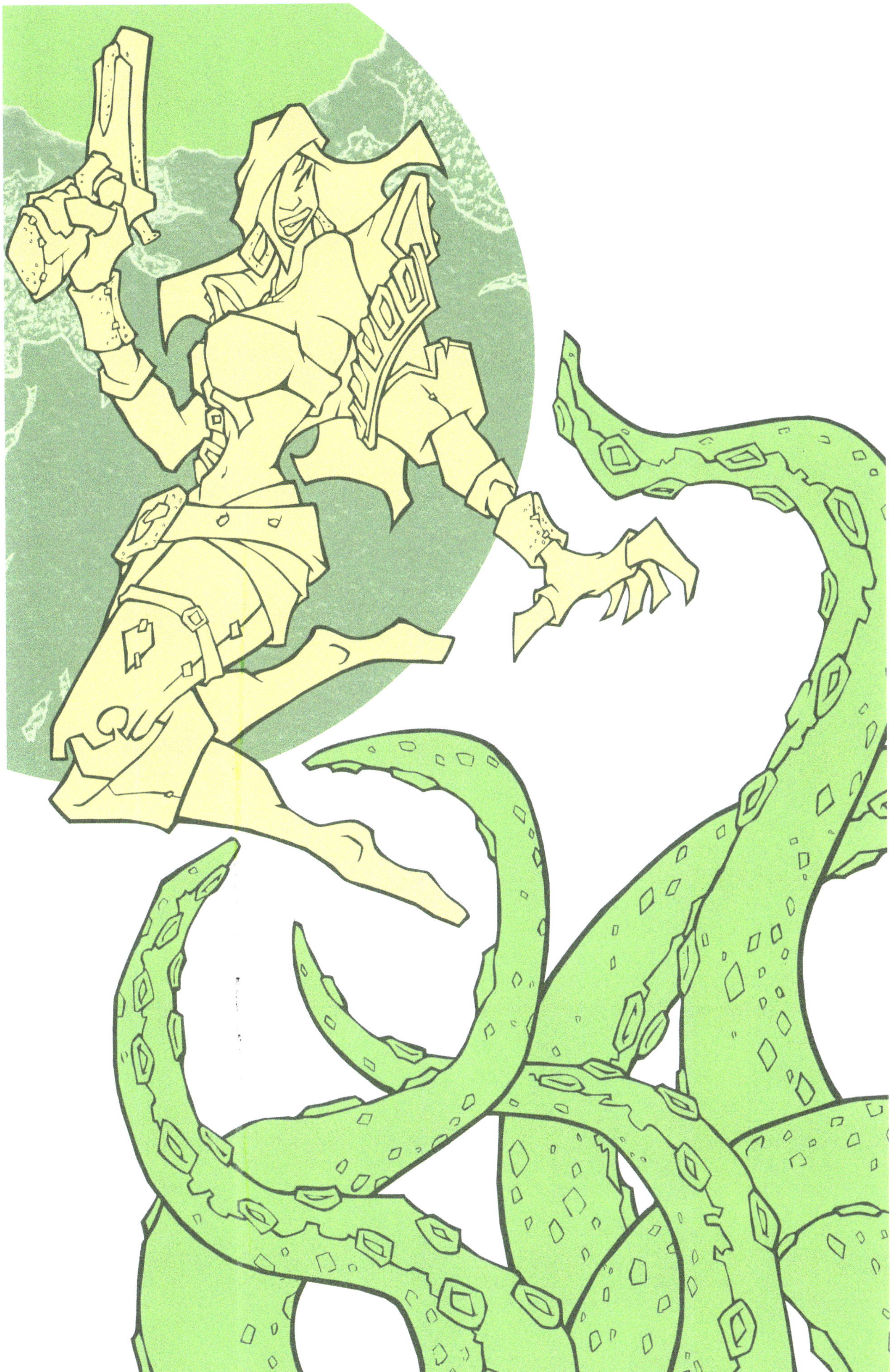

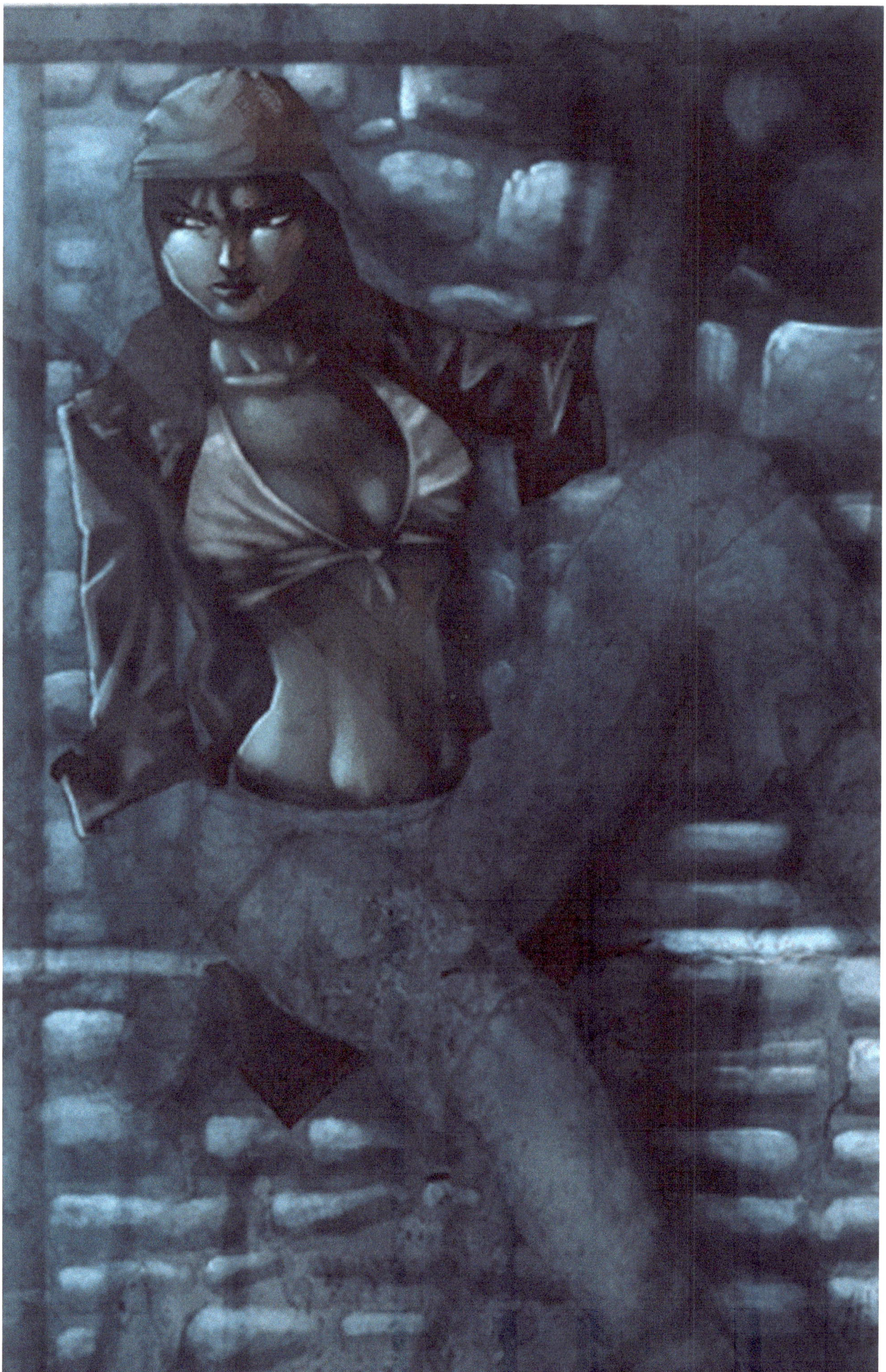

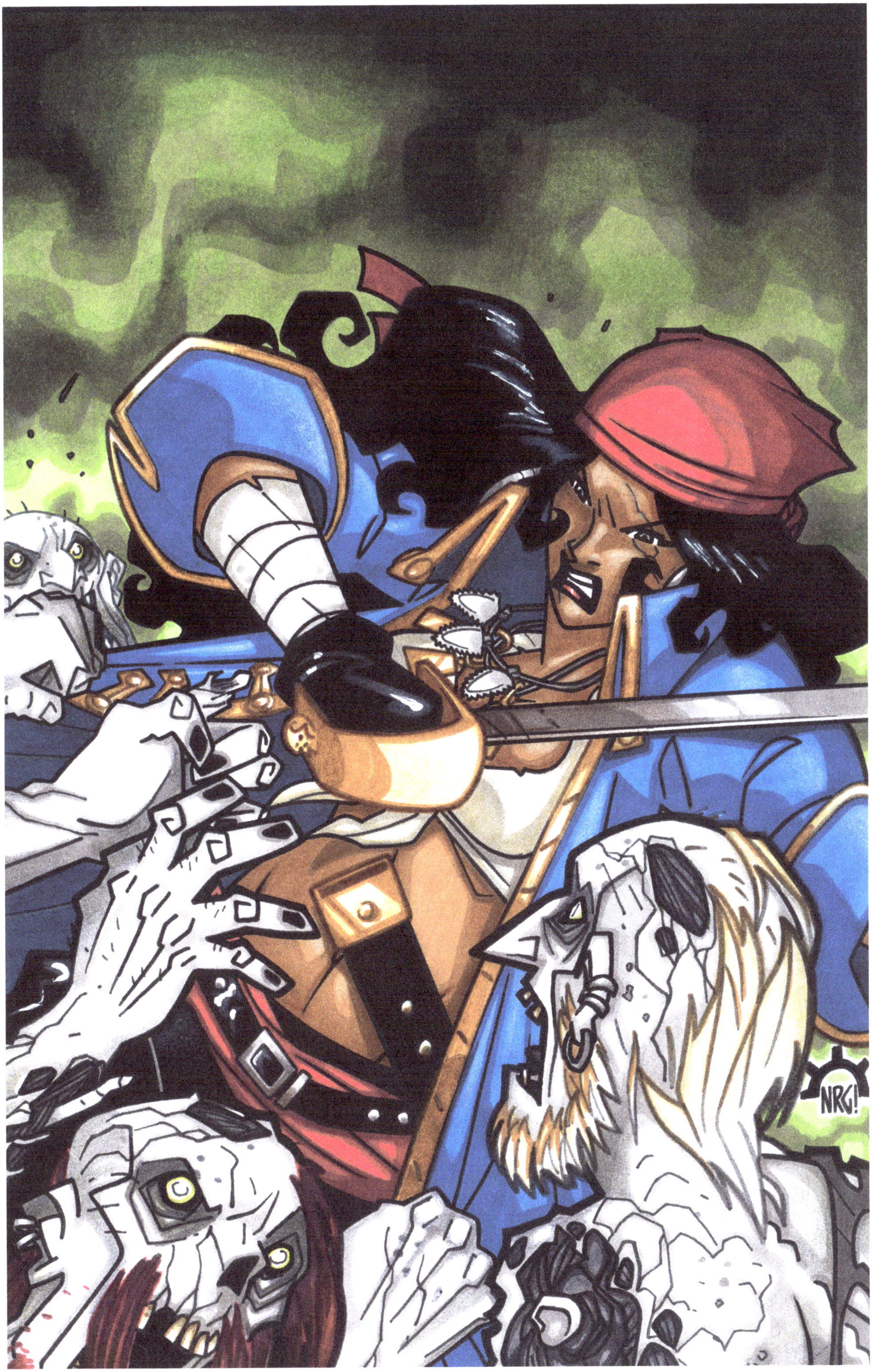
NRG!

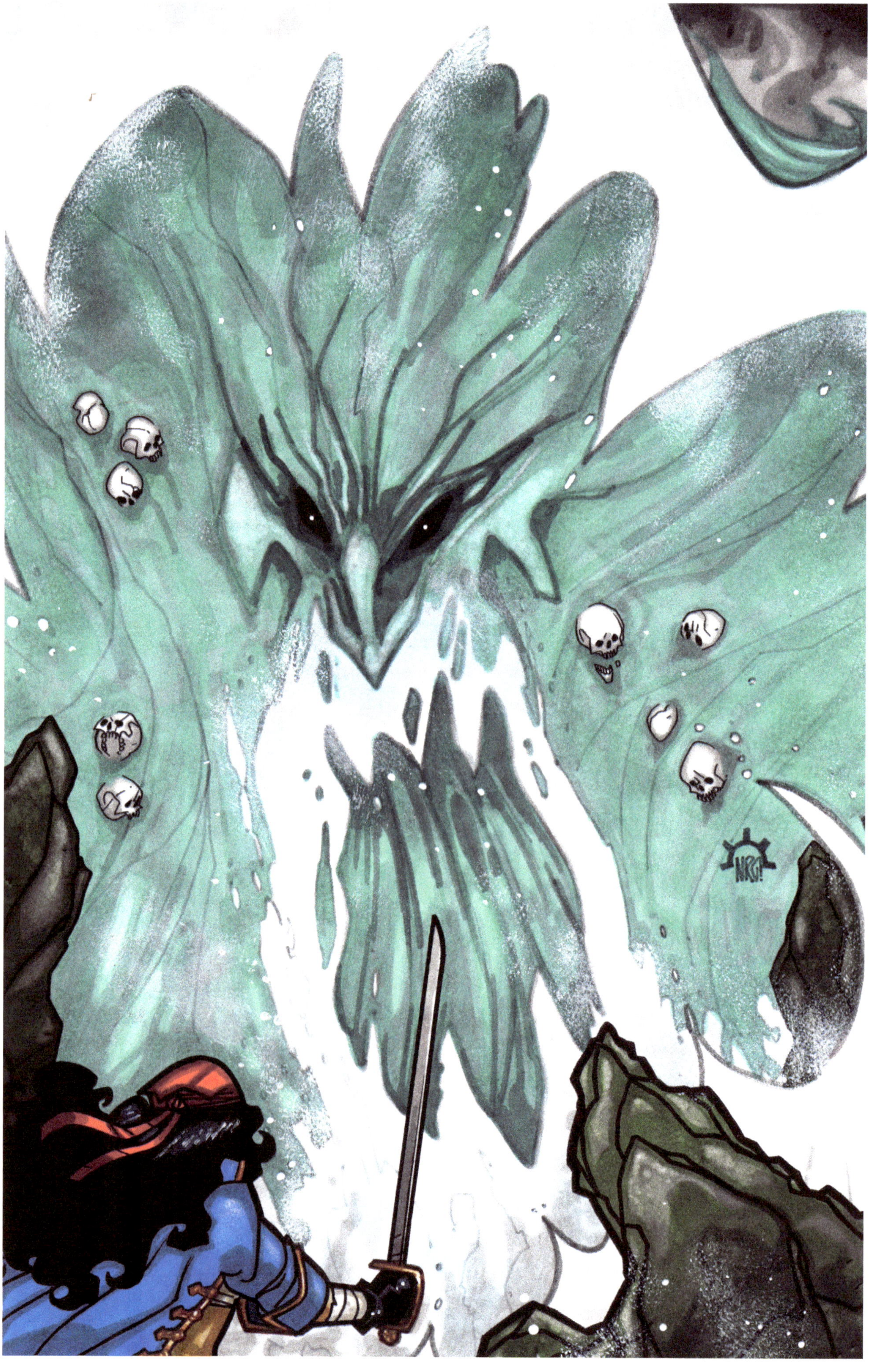

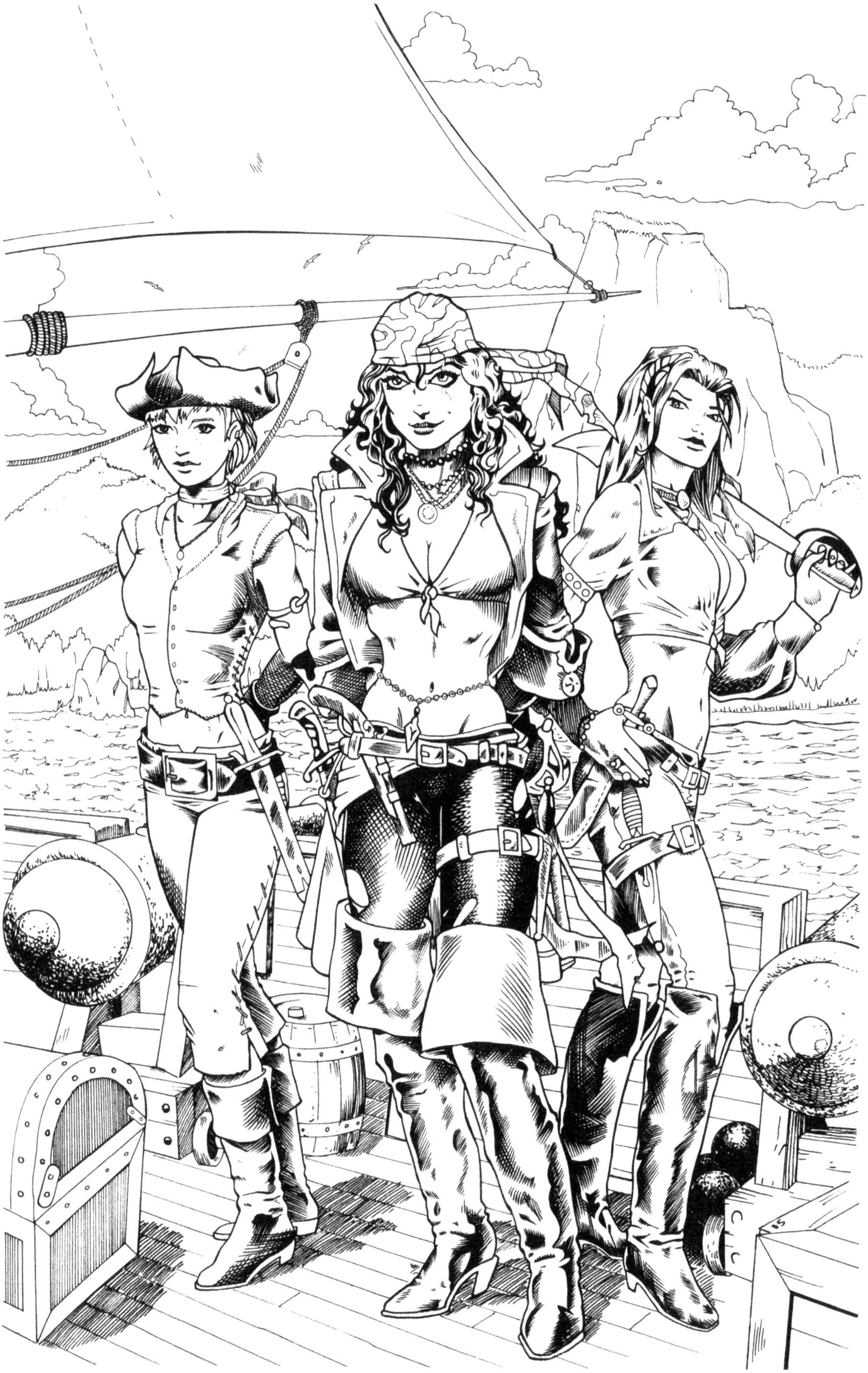

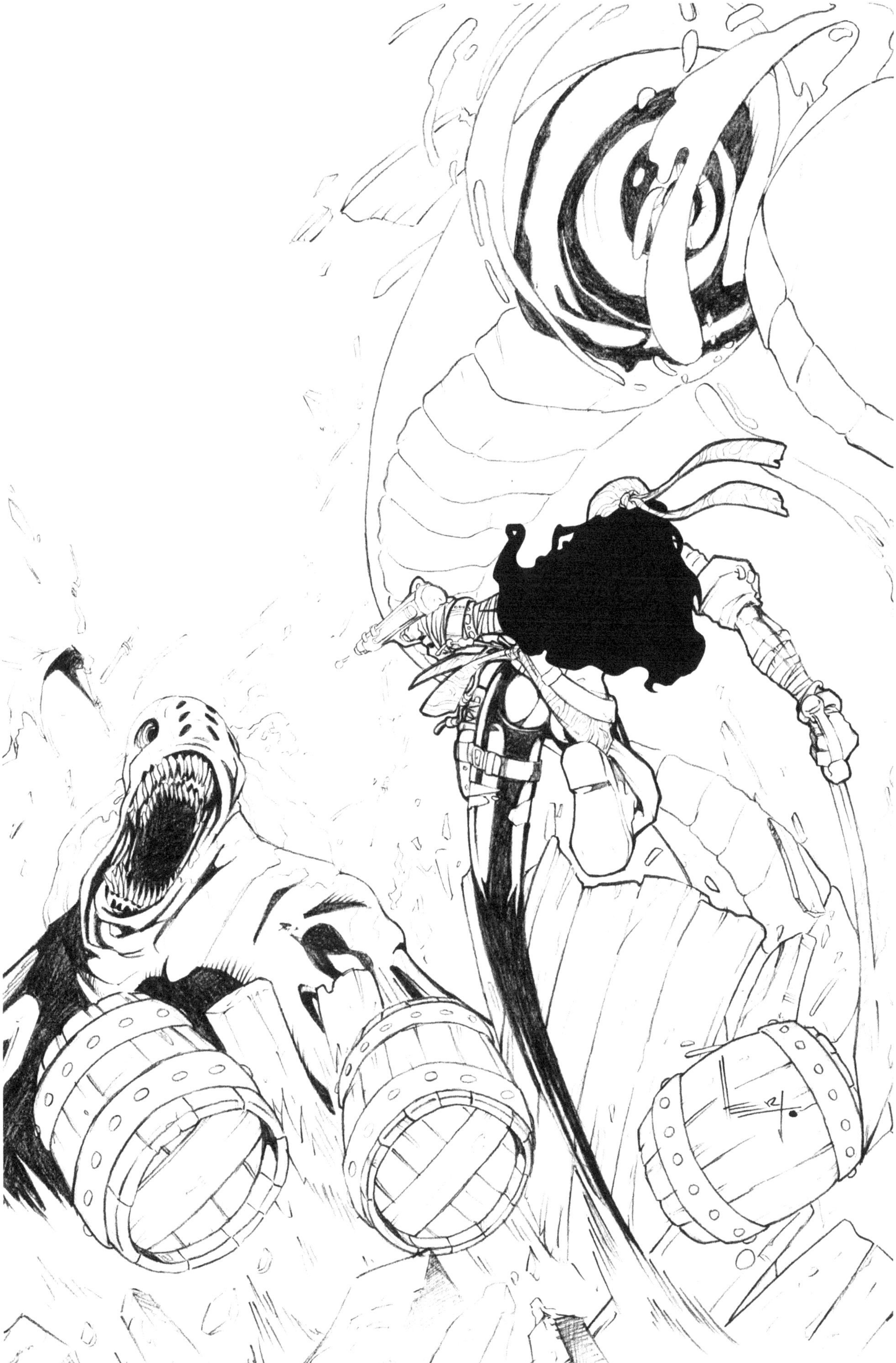

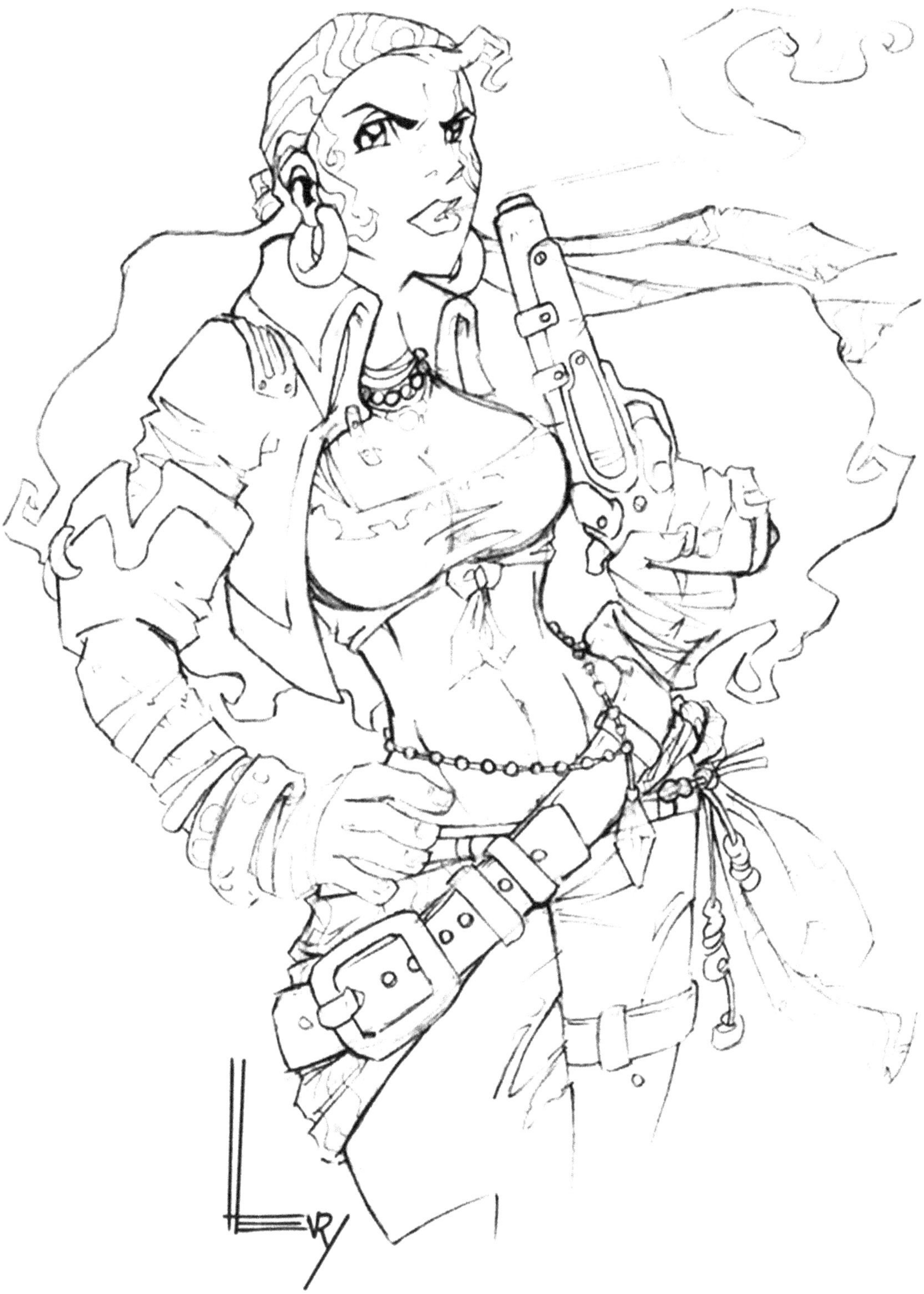

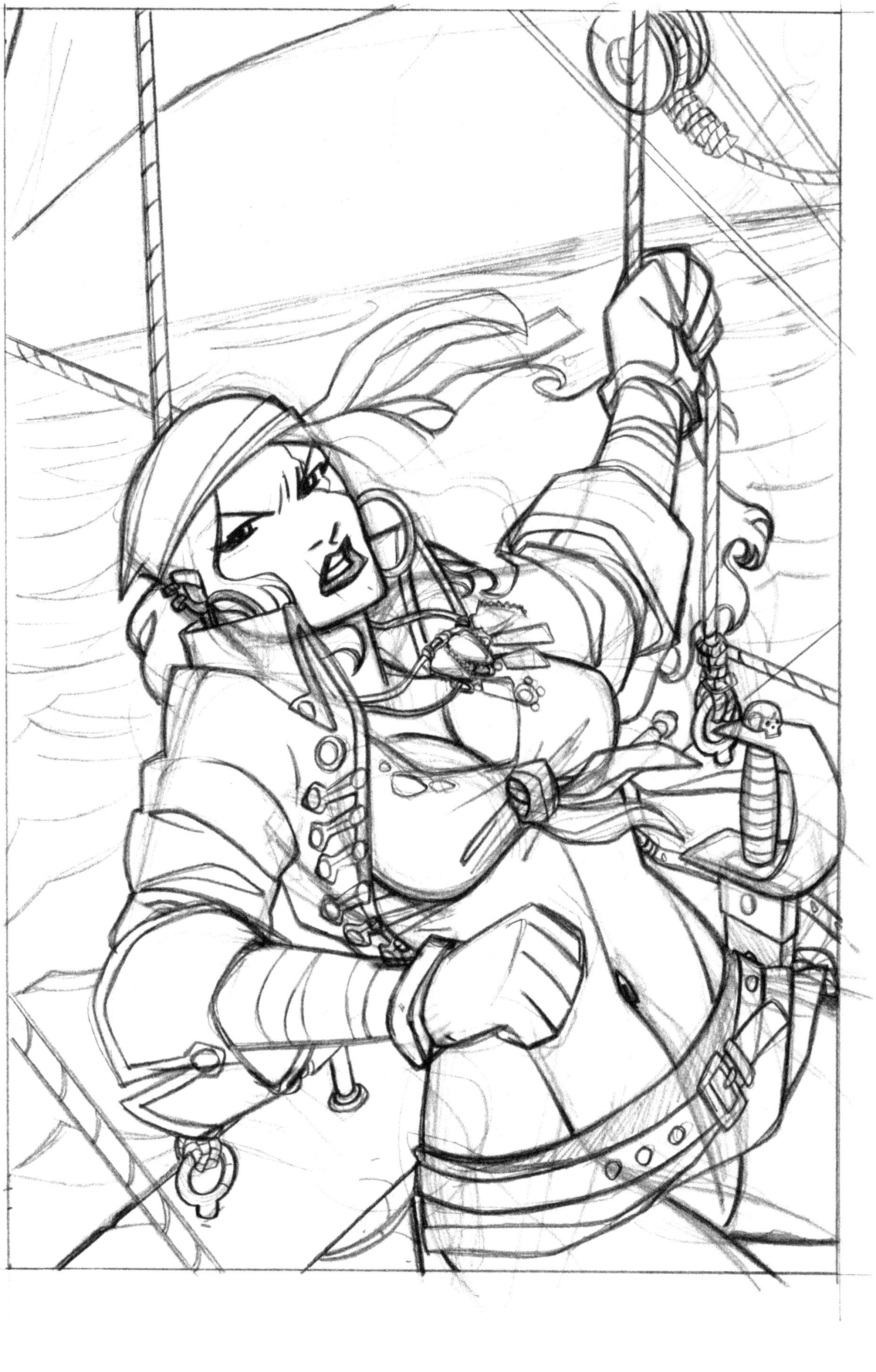

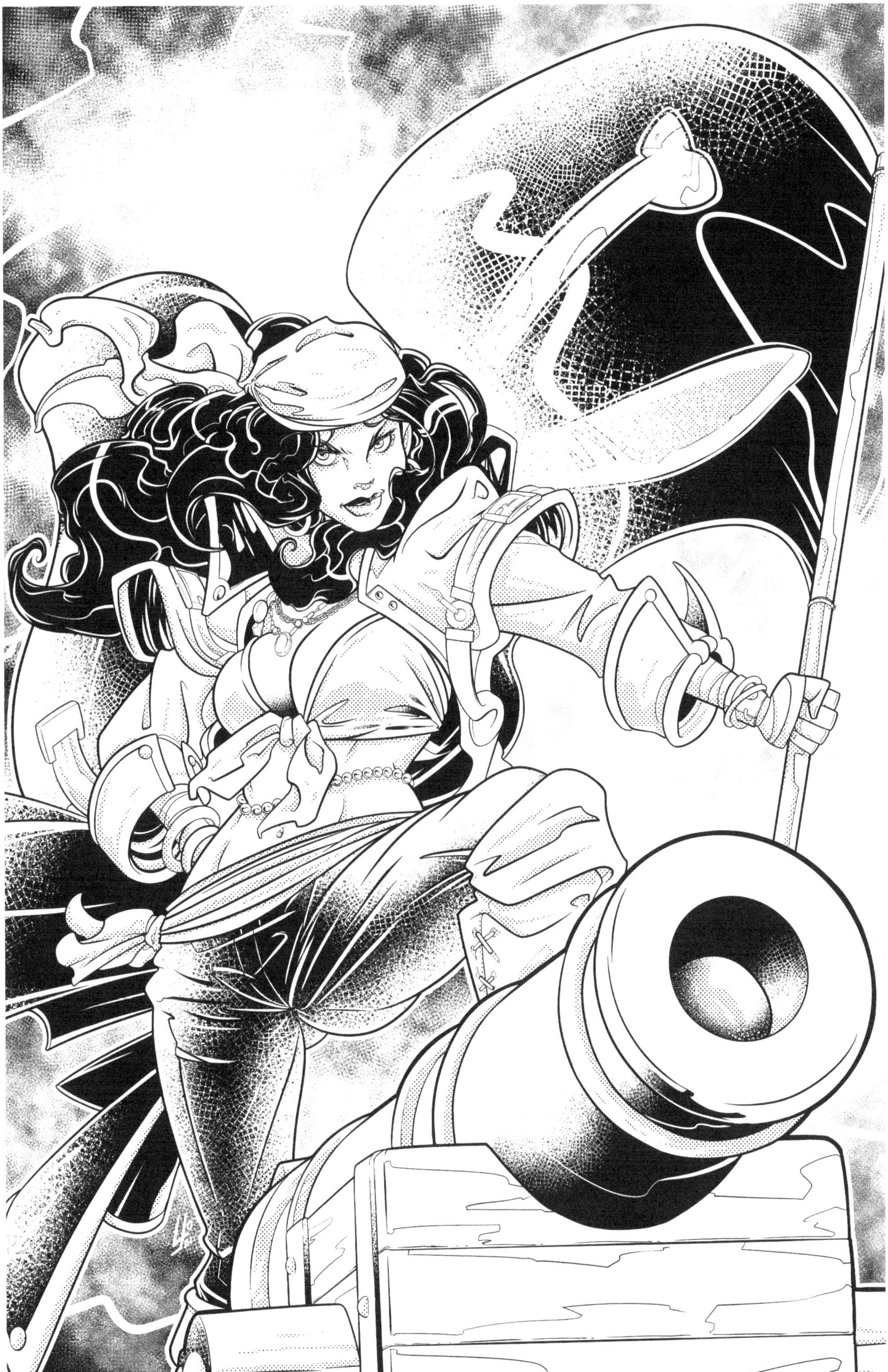

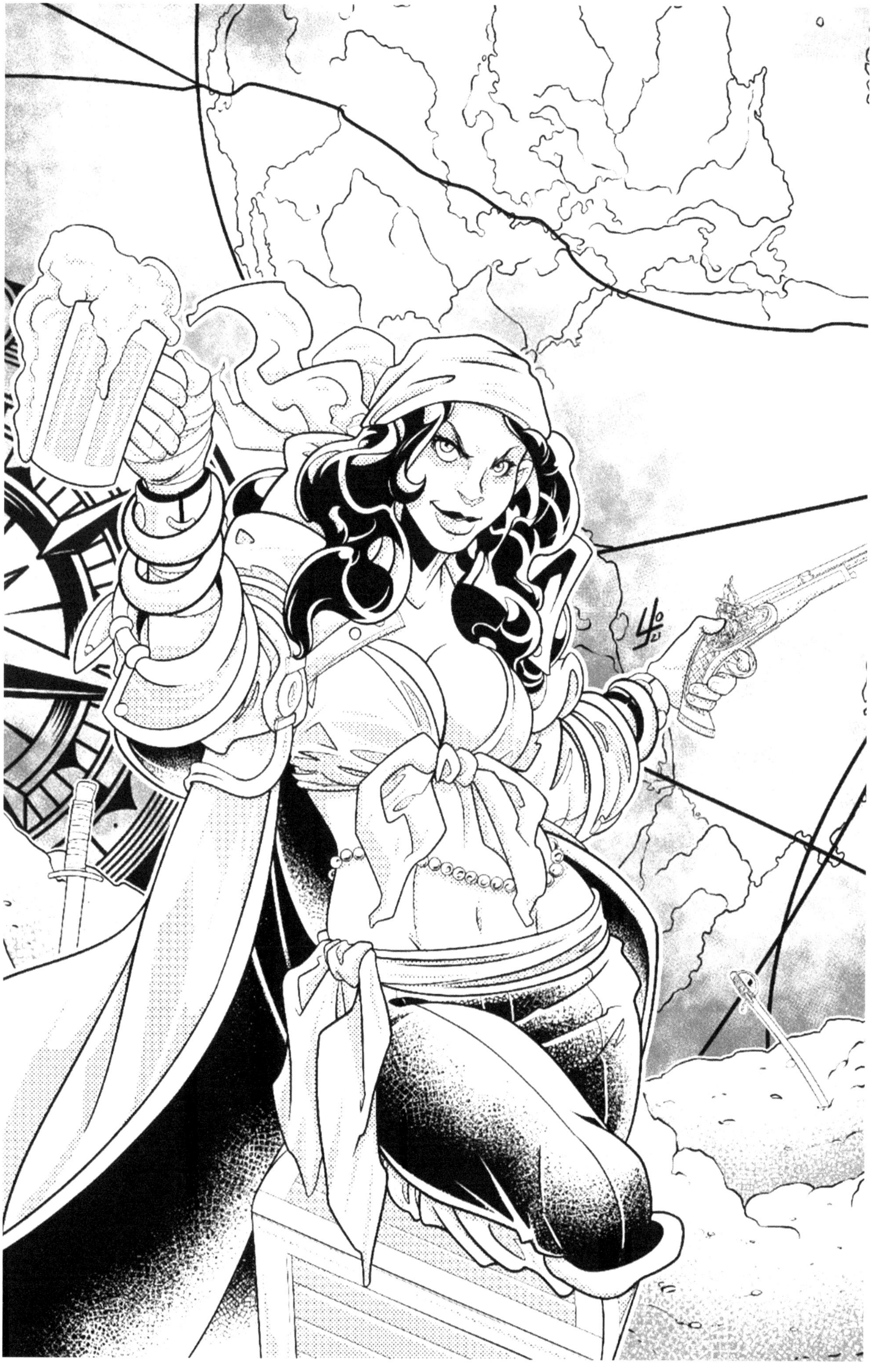

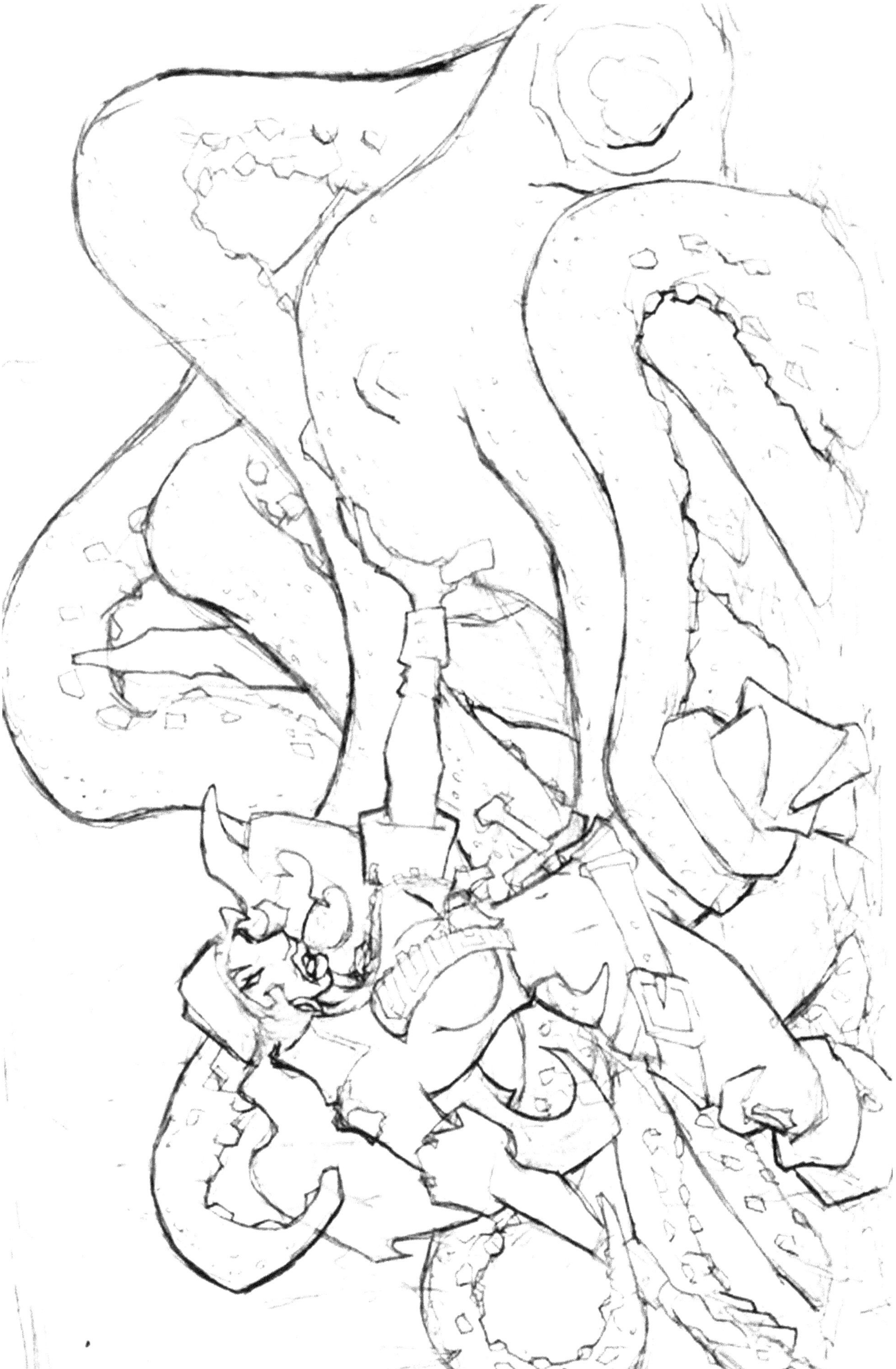

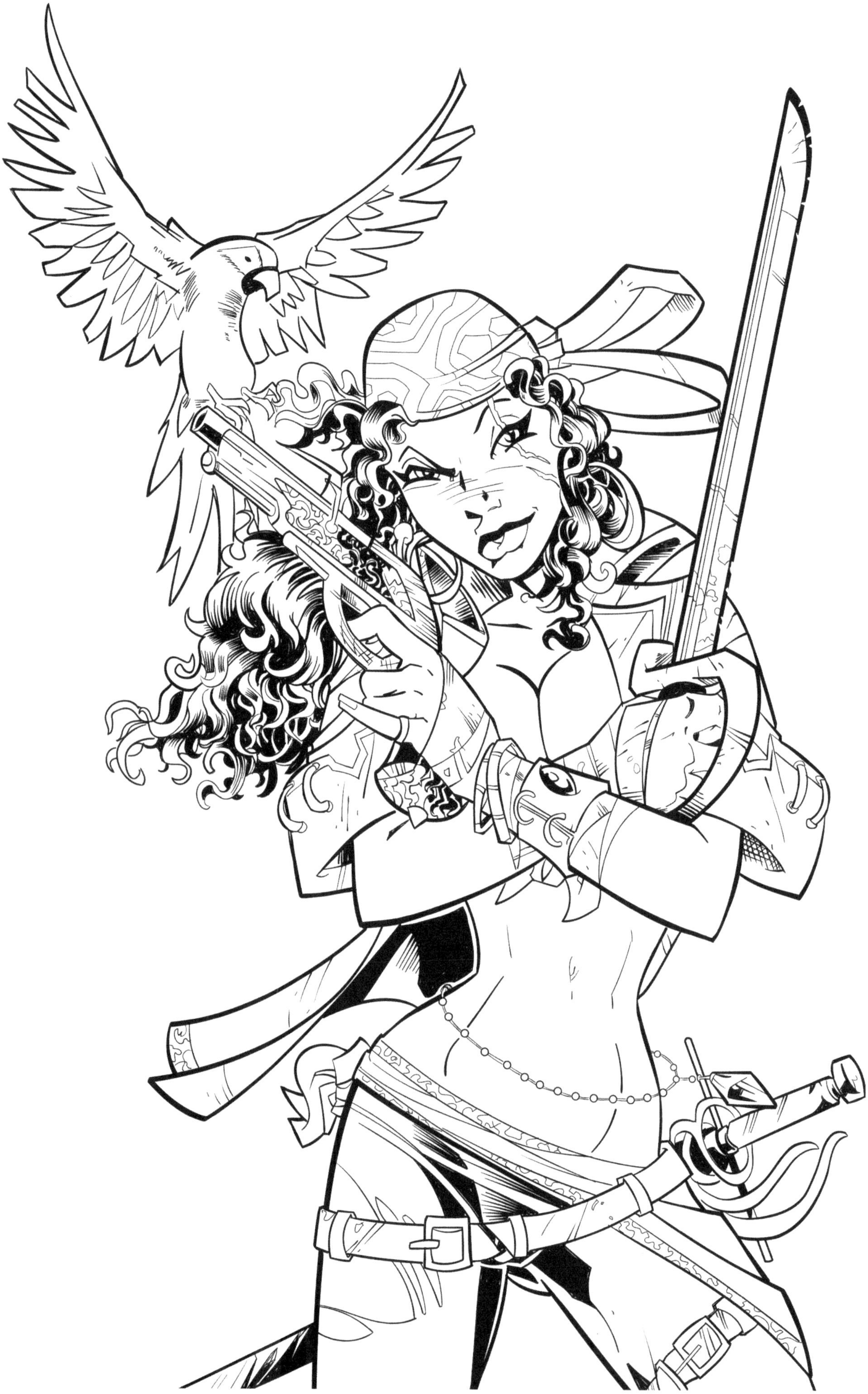

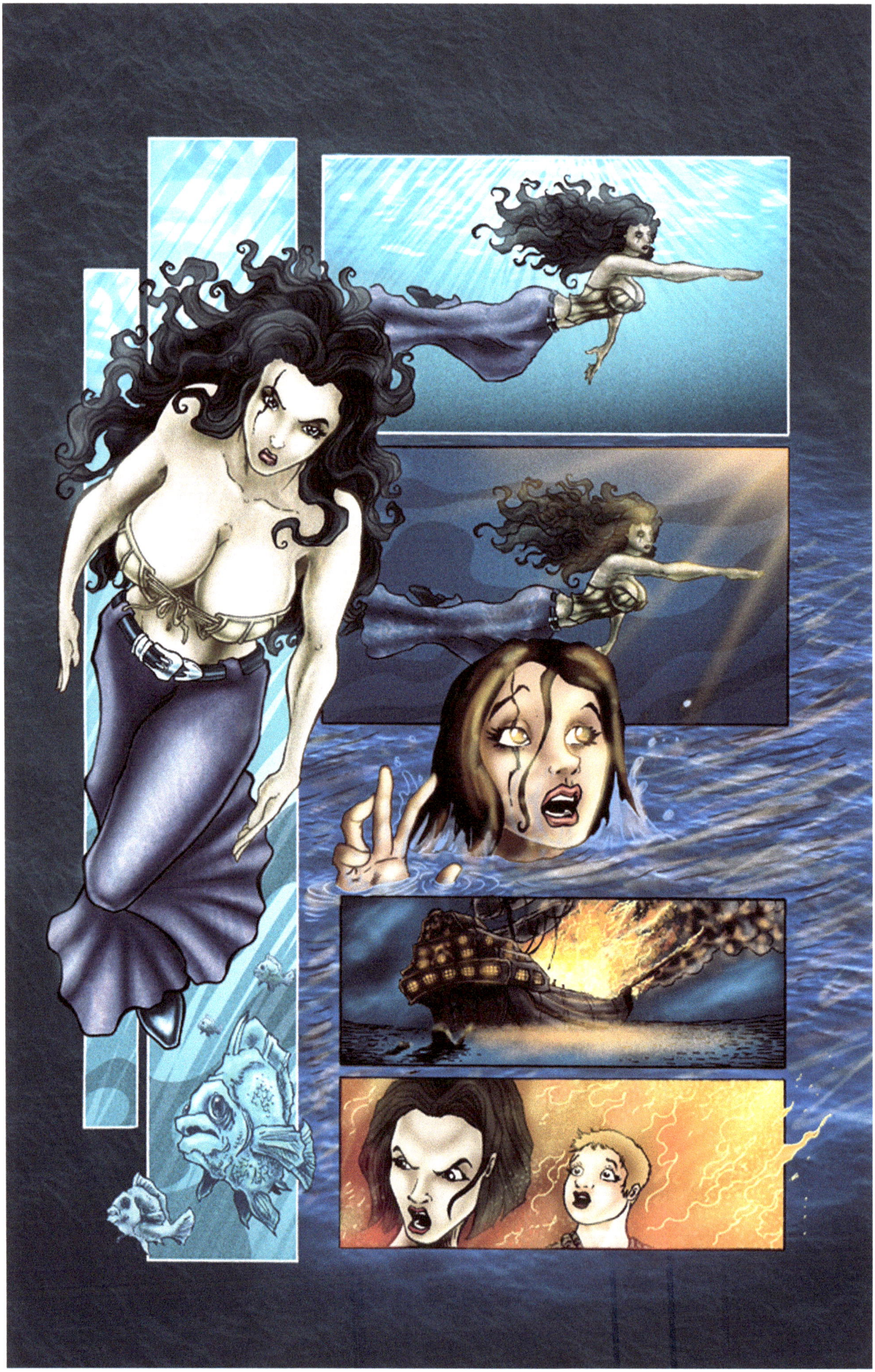

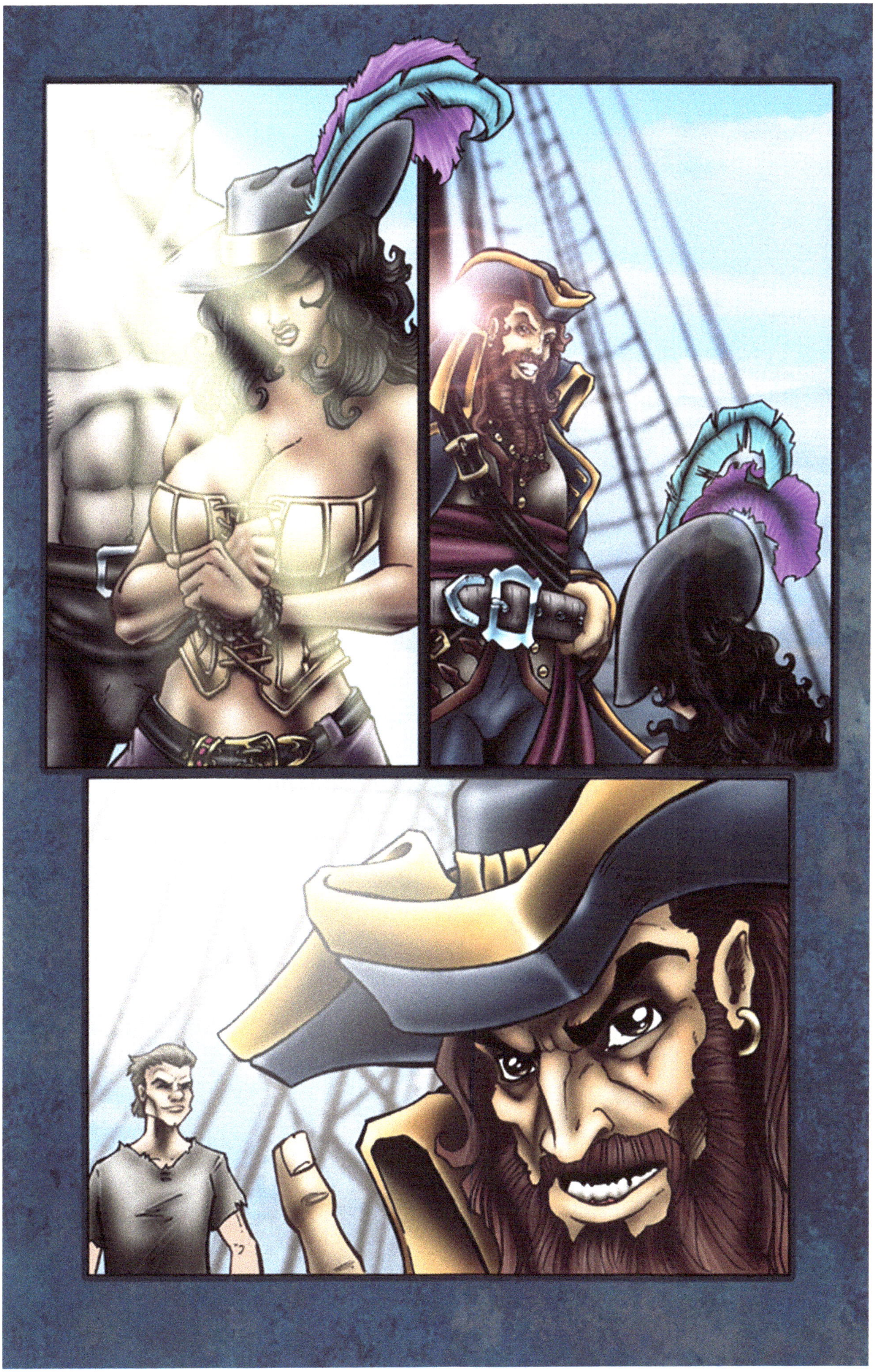

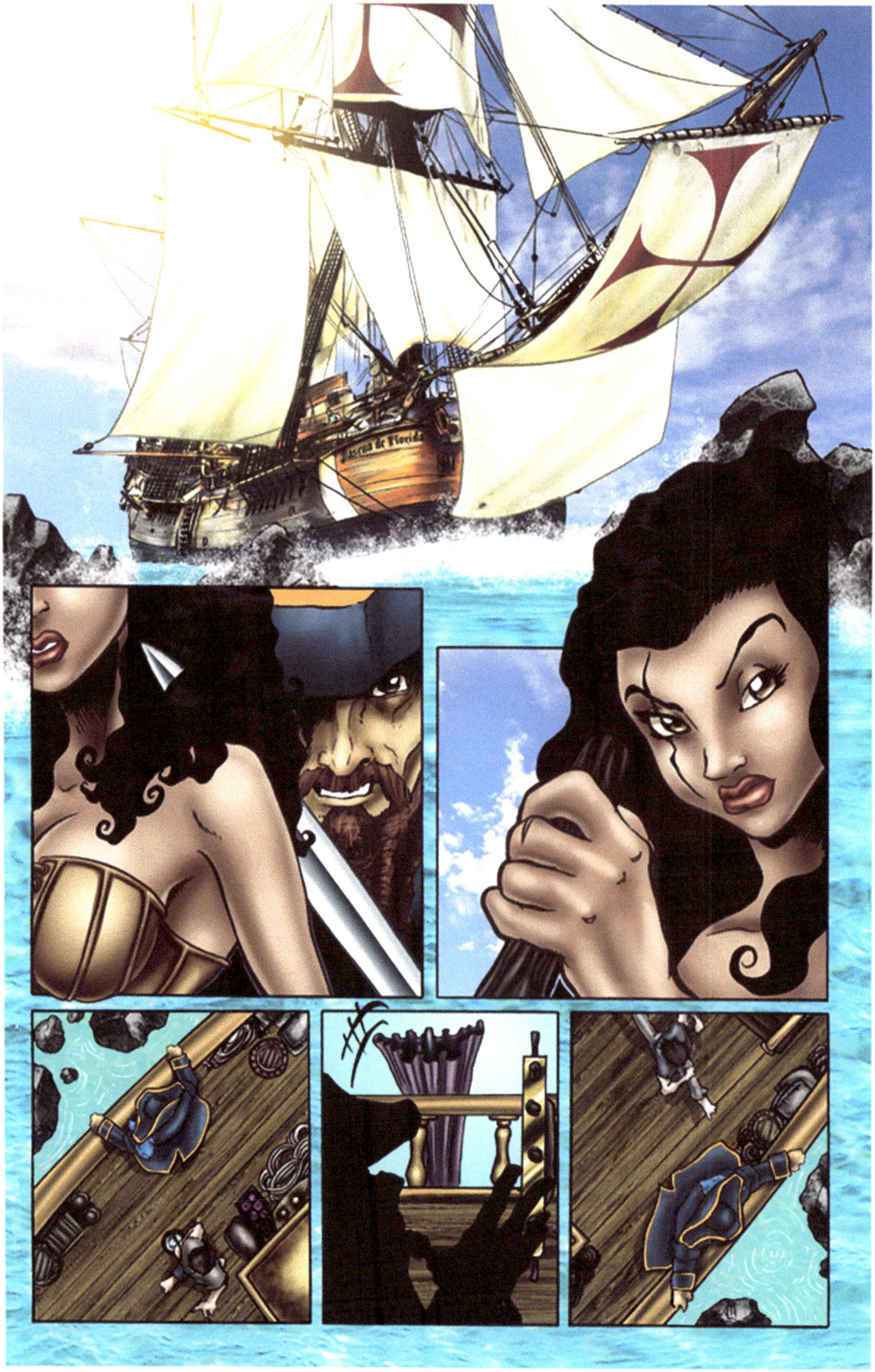

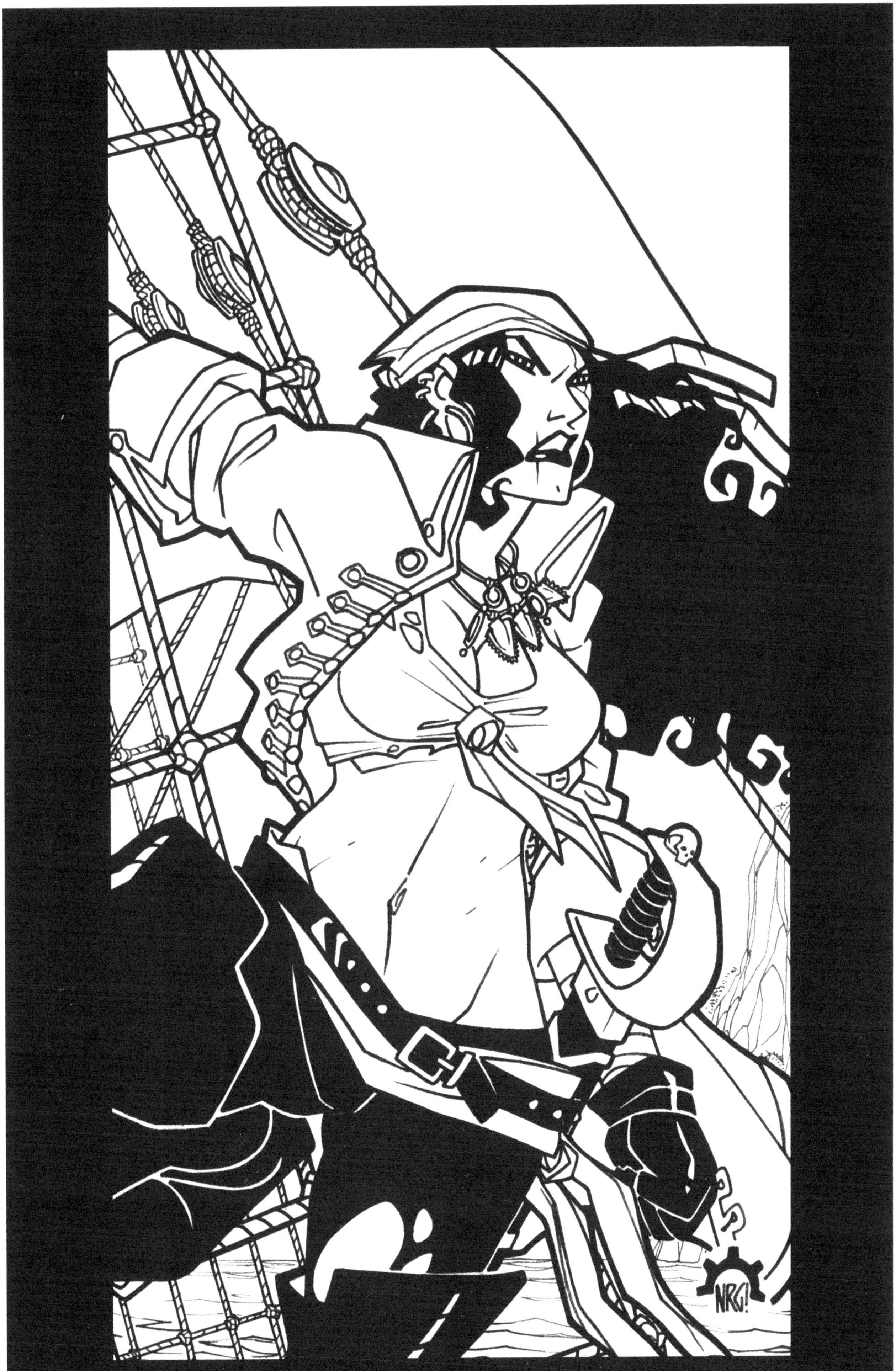
NRG!

TIDALWAVE COMICS

Writer: Darren G. Davis, Scott Davis, Eric Arvin, Andrew Shayde, JS Earls

Art: Mike Maydak, Diego Simone, Nicolas Giacondino, Mik Jimenez

Letters: Benjamin Glibert, Chris Studabaker, Warren Montgomery

Colors: Andrew Cramer, Diego Simone, Fernando Martinena, Mike Maydak

Cover: Yonami

Special Thanks to all the pin-up artists!

Darren G. Davis — Publisher
Maggie Jessup — Publicity
Susan Ferris — Entertainment Manager
Steven Diggs Jr. — Marketing Manager

TIDALWAVE PRODUCTIONS

THE BLACKBEARD LEGACY AND CONTENTS ARE COPYRIGHT © AND ™ DARREN G. DAVIS. ALL RIGHTS RESERVED. TIDALWAVE IS COPYRIGHT © AND ™ DARREN G. DAVIS. ALL RIGHTS RESERVED. ANY REPRODUCTION OF THIS MATERIAL IS STRICTLY PROHIBITED IN ANY MEDIA FORM OTHER THAN FOR PROMOTIONAL PURPOSES UNLESS DARREN G. DAVIS OR TIDALWAVE PUBLISHING GIVES WRITTEN CONSENT. PRINTED IN THE USA www.tidalwavecomics.com